PRICED ABOVE RUBIES

WOMEN OF THE OLD TESTAMENT

by

Rosi MorganBarry

Published by Feather Books
PO Box 438
Shrewsbury SY3 0WN, UK
Tele/fax; 01743 872177

Website URL: http://www.waddysweb.freeuk.com
e-mail: john@waddysweb.freeuk.com

2000

ISBN: 1 84175 049 2

No. 117 in the Feather Books Poetry Series

INTRODUCTION

The Jewish society portrayed in the Hebrew Bible (the Old Testament) was intensely patriarchal.

The first of the Creation stories states that God created human beings in His own image; in the image of God He created them; male and female He created them ...

(Genesis 1: 27, REV)

Thus asserting plainly that men and women were equal but different. But in spite of the praise lavished on the good housewife in Proverbs (31: 10 - 31) from which the title of this meditation is taken, the Old Testament portrays women as very much secondary in status and ability to men.

It was believed that a woman's primary function was to bear children, and childlessness was a serious social stigma, causing much grief and heart-searching. Women were subservient first to their fathers, then to their husbands. Both husband and father had power of life and death over their wives and daughters. A woman could be part of a polygamous family set-up; bought and sold as a slave, a handmaid or concubine (an arrangement which could never be redeemed, as a man-slave could be redeemed every seventh year); she could be divorced by her husband, but could never divorce him under any circumstances. She had little say in her own destiny; was given little education other than the skills of motherhood and housewifery; could seldom inherit property or manage her own affairs. [1]

She was held to be ritually "unclean" by the very nature of her womanhood, and could therefore never serve in any priestly capacity. In the later development of Jewish worship, women were barred from all except the outer areas of the Temple, and prevented from taking part in the services of the synagogue.

Most of the pen-pictures of women in the Old Testament are shadowy portraits, in contrast to the characters of the men: patriarchs, soldiers, judges, prophets, priests and kings who emerge as real people, unequivocally portrayed with all their faults and foibles as well as greatness of soul and mind.

The women described in these verses have been fleshed out (with considerable, and perhaps unfounded flights of imagination) from their sketchy Bible pictures. Here we have three queens; a prophetess; one of Israel's judges; ordinary wives and mothers; a widow, and two slave-girls. I have used feminine intuition to indicate that all these women may have come to their own ideas about God and His dealings with the female half of His creation, through their own intensely womanly experiences - which run the gamut of emotion from terror to exultation.

Although they were women of their times and bound to (and hidebound by) their culture, their insights into aspects of the God's nature as they understood it, may have been very different from those of the men who shaped our Jewish and Christian theology. But they seem to me to carry their own validity. I leave them to speak from their own times - and for themselves.

¹ There were a few exceptions to this: Job's daughters were given equal shares in their father's inheritance with their brothers, and Numbers 27: 7 - 8 explains that a daughter could inherit if there no sons, but she had to marry a member of her own tribe in order to keep the property in the family.

BIBLE REFERENCES:

Hagar:	Genesis 12: 10-20, 16: 1-15, 21: 8-21.
Leah and Rachel:	Genesis 29, 30, 35: 16-29
Miriam:	Exodus 2: 7, 15: 20-21; Numbers 12
Deborah:	Judges 4: 1-23
A girl without a name	Judges 19
Hannah:	1 Samuel 1, 2: 1-11; 18-21
Jezebel:	1 Kings 16: 29-33; 17: 1; 18; 19: 1-3; 21; 2 Kings 9: 30-37
The widow at Zarephath:	1 Kings 17: 7-24
Vashti and Esther:	The two books of Esther.

WOMEN OF THE BIBLE
THE OLD TESTAMENT

HAGAR
The Book of Genesis

I, Hagar, am old now, and looking back
    can see the pattern of the distant years.

I have a sense of purpose and of plan,
    as though some Mind, some Hand, had pulled the threads
    of all our lives, and deftly wove them through
    and round each other. Much as I used to weave
    the coloured strands on our narrow desert looms,
    to make the patterned strips for our best garments.

My thread was dark, while she, even in later years
    was all bright gold; yet woven together
    with Abraham, with our sons, we made
    an inevitable pattern. Useless to ask
    could it have all been different? I have learned
    some little store of wisdom, and I know
    the Mind that forms the pattern needs the dark
    to balance out the coloured and the light.

I am content now, watching my grandsons play,
    to be the dark shadow, the background thread
    on which the stripes are set.

It was not always so. My father was
    a minor civil servant at the Pharaoh's
    court. His temper was short-fused,
    and for a misdemeanour he was stripped
    of title, goods and office. We, his family,
    became the king's chattels. That was the time
    Abram had come to Egypt, and Sarai lived
    in the king's palace. There was some fuss

about her, I don't know what it was;
except the king was angry and ordered
Abram to go, and take her; and to ensure
his going, plied him with gold and silver,
wheat, fruit and wine, cattle, sheep -
and me. A child not ten years old, I was
in Pharaoh's gift. And so became handmaid
to Sarai.

What was she like, you ask? Well, beautiful -
although in middle age - and with that arrogance
common to lovely women, who think the world
owes them due homage. Abram adored her.

But they were strange, these Hapiru,
who roamed the country, settling nowhere
for longer than one grass season. Abram had
ideas about One God, who talked with him
of claiming land and fathering a race.

There was, he said, only One God. Strange to me.
In Egypt we had many: Re-of-the-Sun,
Sky-Goddess Nut, her husband Ged-of -Earth,
Isis, Osiris, Horus and Hathor - many more
of many shapes and forms. Later, I came to know
of Abram's Only God, and His beneficence.

But that was after I'd been made to serve
Abram's obsession. Sarai had no child,
and she decreed that I, her slave, should be
surrogate mother. I had no choice
but to submit to the old man's embrace
and bear the task of mother of his race.

Ah, how I triumphed in my pregnancy!
>What did I hope for? Status perhaps;
>to be accorded more than mere commands;
>perhaps some notice from her. Well,
>that I had, but spiced with jealousy.

If she ignored me then, she hated now,
>and Abram, kind to me but weak to her
>gave me no help. And so I fled -
>into the desert.

Sick, tearful, I headed out for home,
>even death seemed better than the lash
>of Sarai's tongue. At the well (now called
>Beer-Lahai-Roi), at my lowest point
>with all hope gone - there I met The Lord.

He asked, as any mortal man would ask:
>"What are you doing here?" His gentle words
>made me spill out my fears, my hatreds,
>sadnesses, despair ... and He
>took all upon Him - and gave me hope.

He said my son would be the first
>of a great nation; would be a wild
>ass of a man, kicking against the odds,
>as even now he kicked against my womb.

El-Roi, the God-Who-Sees, saw all my mind
>and heart - and seemed to set
>some worth on what He found there.
>I went back, submitted to my mistress,
>in time gave birth to Ishmael: "God-has-heard".

The God-Who-Sees was right: he was
    a prickly child, unwilling to make friends.

But as he grew he came to be my shield
    and my defence. Abraham [2] loved us both.

Sarah grew kinder, for she had to submit
    her pride and doubts to her own miracle.
    When she was ninety-eight, Isaac was born.

And Ishmael, my stormy son, adored
his baby brother; spent hours by his cot,
brought gifts - a leaf, a feather; played and
provoked his baby laughter for fretful tears.

And Sarah watched. Fearful, possessive, hard.
    On Isaac's name feast, the day that he was weaned,
    Abraham, exulting in his sons, declared
    a joint inheritance; met with dismay
    Sarah's denial. She was still, even in old age
    the imperious spoilt beauty, who for years
    had her own way. She wanted to be rid
    once and for all, of Ishmael and me.

God acquiesced! And so did Abraham.
Against a hum of protest, which did no more
    than swell to a faint murmur, we were sent
    out to the desert. With little food,
    a skin of water and the clothes we stood in,
    Ishmael and I were banished from the only

---

[2] At this point in the Bible narrative (Genesis 17) their names were changed from "Abram" (= High Father) to "Abraham" (= Father of Many) and "Sarai" (= Mockery) to "Sarah" (= Princess).

home he had ever known. At first we tried
to cheer each other on, but when the last drop
of water had been drunk, thirst and weariness
reduced my valiant boy to childish tears.
He could not think what he had done!
I could not tell him that in this cruel world
simply to be - for some - was fault enough.

I left him weeping. Where now the God-Who-Sees?
The One I once believed put value on
my life, and his? Do not the gods play senet [3]
with us? Shifting us, their creatures
about the world at whim?

But I was answered. God saw; He also heard;
He brought us up again from deep despair,
showed me a well of water, life and hope.

I am as old now, as Sarah was
when she had Isaac.

I have known envy of my son's young wife;
possessiveness which fiercely would defend
my grandsons' futures. Looking back,
the pattern becomes plain. It does not justify
her cruelty, but weaves it an inevitable thread
to make the cloth complete. God's Hand and Eye
is on us all. My children's children,
as much as hers, are under His concern.
In that I rest content. [4]

---

[3] Senet is a game, rather like chess, which was played in ancient Egypt.

[4] The Arab nation declares itself descended from Hagar's son Ishmael; the Jews claim Isaac as their forefather. Both were sons of Abraham; Arabs and Jews are therefore brother nations.

LEAH - AND RACHEL
The Book of Genesis

"He was mine - from the beginning".
That's what she used to say.

Well, she saw
him first, going to water our father's sheep
in the late afternoon, with the hot sun
throwing long purple shadows of rock and tree.
He was weary, travel-stained, and in his face
she saw some hint of trouble, and the sadness
we later learned he had left behind. He heaved
the stone from the well-mouth for her, helping
to draw the water for the thirsty flocks.
And from that moment all his love was hers -
and hers alone.

You think it was easy having a younger sister?
And one who was lively, bright, and quite considerably
prettier in all respects? I may have been soft-eyed,
but otherwise my homely looks and dumpy
figure caused my father to despair
of ever finding me a husband.

And when
our mother died, I was the one who ran
the household: ground and baked our bread;
carded and dyed and spun and wove our clothes;
stretched out the tent-hides; hauled wood
and water; trimmed the lamps; searched far
and wide for healing herbs; milked goats;
made cheeses; grew our vegetables, while she
tended our father's flock. Which gave her leave

to flirt with all the shepherd boys of Haran.

I used to scold her, but she would laugh
and tease, and call me jealous. So I was,
but under that I loved her, my poor Rachel.

Well then - she hauled home her prize:
our cousin Jacob, Aunt Rebekkah's boy.
Having her look about him, father said.
And wouldn't you know, I took one glance at him,
standing tall beside my laughing sister,
and lost my wits and heart together.
                    Not
that I ever dared to tell. I would have been
made a laughing stock. Strange how we plain
and ugly women are not supposed to feel -
only to do. As though our getting on
with routine household tasks would stop the heart
from beating faster, or the mind from spinning
dreams.

I spun and wove her wedding veil;
roasted the lambs, and baked cakes for the feast.
Trying to wish them well, having watched
their love burn and grow through seven years
he served for her bride-price.

            The afternoon
of the wedding day is burned into my mind.

My father called me from my many tasks -
even now, all these years on it seems incredible -
and told me I, the elder, must be married first.

Devious, clever, calculating, cunning!
Later I realised it was his way of worming
seven more years of hard and unpaid labour
out of poor Jacob!

But would you pity me?
I begged to be let out of this situation,
fearing the storm it would provoke. But father
merely laughed and said how else could I
expect a husband - except by proxy
and these dubious means?

So in a fever of fear and a turmoil of
conflicting loves, I went back to my work;
took out my frustration on the dough,
and waited - for Rachel's wedding night.

Next day the brou-ha-ha I feared broke loud
over my head. But Jacob's stormy scenes -
and Rachel's screams and tears - battered against
our father. No more than he deserved.
From that day on we lost, Rachel and I,
all our respect for him.

What ups and downs
we had in our joint marriage to Jacob!
She had his love and his desire, but I -
I had his children.

It was as though
this God whom Abraham knew and Isaac feared
was minded to give to me - plain homely Leah,
the blessings of a wife, leaving Rachel
frustrated and cross. And sharp-tongued,

as only she could be when thwarted.

But
things worked out amicably enough. For Jacob,
my six sons and a daughter, and the children
of our servant girls, were balanced by
his love for Rachel's Joseph. What will become
of that spoiled brat I dread to think.

The years
rolled on. Jacob, by careful bargaining
and clever husbandry, increased our flocks
and herds, and sought to leave our father Laban.
He, Jacob, had once made a pact -
a bargain with his God to take us back
to Isaac's land. Rachel and I, united
in resentment of our father's treatment,
cheerfully put together all we had:
tents, clothes, looms, pots, sheep,
goats - and children. And Rachel in a sudden
spurt of spite stole father's household gods.

When he came roaring after us - and them,
she sat on them! But then we had long lost
belief in these quaint, quirky bits of wood.
Jacob's ideas of One Great Only God,
invisible but knowable, had caught our minds.

We did not need to wrestle with ideas
of God, as Jacob did at Peniel.
As women, deeply concerned with procreation,
we knew, or rather felt we understood
how the Creator Spirit laboured to call

the world and all its creatures into being.

And how He calls us back to Himself in death.
Like Rachel now, struggling with her last breath
to give her second much desired son his life.

I have given her syrup of poppies to ease her pain.

We will mourn her together, Jacob and I. Here,
at Bethlehem-Ephrathah she will sleep
her last sleep; and Bethlehem will ever
for her sake be remembered.

MIRIAM
The Books of Exodus and Numbers

So. I am to be out cast. For a while.
in one sense all we women
at frequently recurring times
experience in our lives this knowingness
of exclusion. And according to
the Laws my brother - what's the word? -
devised? Drew up? Received?
this is a legal matter. A code of practice
for keeping women in their rightful place.

No - that is perhaps too much.
even for me, jealous and embittered
as I am. So - I have seven days
of pain and loneliness in which to work
on what I am, and what I know.

Day One.
     The desert heat burns under my feet.

Memories of cool water flooding in
like the Nile tide. My mother's tears,
as she committed baby Moses to its care;
and then, not daring to invoke the Egyptian
gods, and perhaps not quite trusting
the invisible God of Abraham our father,
(and after all, where had God been these past
four hundred years?) setting me to watch
for human aid.

     Which came wandering in
as lovely Princess Asath - sister to Pharaoh,
with maids and semi-men; fine-linen fluttering,
a crowd of butterflies among the reeds.
And I, homespun and homely, found my moment
of cleverness on behalf of my beloved
baby brother.

Then came the months of running to and fro
between two worlds, slipping across
the marble threshold and through filmy
curtains, into the dust and heat and smell
of sweaty, flyblown Israel. And back from Hebrew
women crying, despairing, over dead babies,
to one soft-shrouded in the silken lap
of royal Egypt.

     Huge question marks
hung in my head. Why did so many die?
and why was one retrieved? To be the means
of saving all the rest?

Day Two.
    I am thirsty and my skin
crawls with disease. I was never fussy
over washing, never had the way
of easy access to clean water. But
I could use some now. I am loathsome
to myself. If Moses' God intended
my suffering as the means of my salvation,
how will He know when I have suffered enough?

He had grown too tall, my brother,
for Egypt's court. His mind had ranged
beyond its perfumed pampered air, and found
his kinship with beleaguered Israel.
Anger flared up: his own, and Pharaoh's - and
he fled to Midian.
                    From whence he came
with brain aflame and talk of burning. God
in a fire of zeal to save the sons of Jacob.

The King, of course, he would have none of it.
"Who is this Lord that I should heed his voice?
I do not know this God; I will not let
His people go."

So then began the plagues. Designed to wring
his heart - and call the curse
of all the people on him.

Pharaoh you see, is held responsible
for all that comes to Egypt: war or flood,
famine or plague - or goodly harvest.
And this - this obdurate King will have his name

scratched out of Egypt's history. While we,
despairing, desperate, ill-kempt, dirty Jews
will rise triumphant! Into our finest hour!

Day Three.
        Aaron has brought me manna
And a skin of goat's milk. He shares my guilt,
But not my punishment. I am too weary
To concern myself with rights and wrongs of that.

Where was I? Ah! those plagues! The first the worst.
The cool blue Nile turned dark and brown and thick
like blood not water - so that its frogs
crawled over the land, and died in thousands.

Their stinking bodies writhed with maggots; turning
to flies that clustered thick on man and beast
feasting on salty sweat. And still the King,
remaining obstinate, would not let us go.

So then a sooty blight blackened the crops,
and everyone, weakened by poisoned food,
burst out in blistering skin and painful boils.

I can feel sympathy. My leprous body
itches and festers in the desert heat.

Then Egypt's sky rained ice, battering down
the growing wheat. And locusts swarmed, devoured
all that was left. And Pharaoh cried to Moses
to call a halt. But changed his mind. So God
gave darkness for three days of daylight; thick
tangible, choking and close, and Egypt
could not see its hand before its face.

But still he would not let us go.

I wonder now
whether he saw himself engaged in cosmic
war? Pharaoh, god-king representing Ra,
the great, the sun-god, while Moses stood
between him and this so-called God-Without-
A-Name. If so, it was a war he could
not hope to win. For then there came
the last, most dreadful, inexplicable ...

Day Four.
I shiver in the cold
of a desert dusk, and at the memory
of that last eerie night in Egypt.

A dark
Angel passed over us - whose doors were marked
with blood, and struck down all the first
of Egypt's sons. My neighbour lost her husband,
brother, son. And Moses mourned the nephew
he had known, Egypt's Prince.

And so we fled,
grabbing our pots and pans, our half-made bread,
our stomachs hard with fear and bitter herbs,
our joy, clouded with Egypt's pain.

From Rameses
to Succoth, then by way of wilderness
to the Sea of Reeds. And there the last great wonder.

People say now, looking down the years
with knowledge of hindsight, that far out

in distant oceans, mountains heaved and burst
with fire and ashes, blotting out the sun,
and causing seas to swell and fall away
into dry land.
        That may be so. How should
I know what explanations men can make?
But this I see: the miracle lies in the time
these earth events occurred. Egypt pursuing
her Israelite slaves fell under the falling wall
of water, where hours before we all had walked
dry-shod.

Day Five.
        This day dawns bright and clear
as that on which we sang and danced to God.
and I, swung by the music into prophecy,
gave Israel the refrain: "The Lord in triumph
hurled horse and rider down into the sea!"

But looking back across our wandering years,
learning God's Laws from Moses; His codes for conduct,
His rules for minds and hearts, does He not want
us to feel pity rather than rejoice
in Egypt's downfall?

We, His special people signally failed
again and ever again to heed His words
and keep His covenant. And He was harsh
with us. Reminded us in hunger, thirst,
dust, blood and heat that He, and only He,
the Lord of Abraham, could meet our needs.
And only Moses, humble and obedient, could see
Him. Face to face....

Day Six

      ... which made us jealous. Aaron -
and me. Had <u>we</u> not heard the Lord?
had <u>we</u> not prophesied? Had we not kept
our bloodline pure? And so we criticised
our brother Moses. Finding petty excuses
about his foreign wife to vilify
his name. And God was angry. So I,
as woman, bore the punishment. If I had roused
my father's anger, I would be banished
out of his house for seven days. So seven days
outside the camp: sickly, contagious, leprous,
I must remain.

Day Seven.

      I have no pride, no hope of joy
in my own gifts. My skin is healed, but marked
with pits and pocks of fallen blemishes. As well
I had no looks, beauty or grace to mourn.

But now I recognise my brother's stature.
He comes himself to bring me back, with care
and kindliness. And all our people waited
for my soul's healing. Which is more
than I deserve. But now, cleansed of my sin
I can take up my tambourine and sing:
"Lord, who is like You, worthy of awe and praise?
In constant love you lead us out, Your people,
redeemed and guided to Your holy place".

DEBORAH
The Book of Judges

"Deborah held court under the Palm of Deborah,
Between Ramah and Bethel. Thus it is written.
She came by wisdom and the Word of God
To be renowned as prophet and as judge.
All Israel (such as it was in those days)
Came to her for arbitration".

I hear the words. I, Deborah,
Was guided by the Ruach of the Lord.
The Spirit of God spoke in me; and through me
Israel's integrity, totally linked
With her security, was once again
Renewed.

I hear my words
Read through the thousand years that separate
My time from yours, in multi-lingual synagogues.

It was a song of triumph as Israel,
Gathering our armed forces under Barak
Set out to battle for what we saw as right.
Our land - God-given - to be defended against
Those who would make us bow to their own gods.
My word from God, El-Elyon, Adonai,
Was: "Turn 0 Israel! Do not choose new gods,
Nor yet consort with demons! Our God
Will fight for you, and bring the enemy
Grovelling to your feet!"

As mountains shook and thunder rolled,
As rain in torrents fell, the Lord

Gave victory to Barak. Quite simply -
Philistian iron chariots, which had struck
Such fear in the heart of Israel, stuck
In the mud!

And Sisera was delivered
Into the hand of a woman - Jael, the wife
Of Heber, the traitor, the Kenite.

I hear my song of triumph.

And wonder how and why an ordinary woman,
As I once was, should have been given wisdom.

Was it to say that God's impartial word
Can come, does come, to those who are prepared
To listen?
Regardless of gender,
Race, status, riches, or even creed?

A GIRL WITHOUT A NAME
The Book of Judges

I have no name, no home, no husband,
children, status - or self-respect.

And I am also dead.

I speak to you from Sheol. I'm not allowed
to tell you more of where I am, nor why.
The story of my life; its consequence,
you need to know - and nothing more.

I can recall the moment of my death.

Before my body sighed its final breath
      my heart had died within me and my mind
      had given up its hold on life. It was
      the moment when the door slammed shut and cut
      me off from hope ....

          *   *   *   *   *

We lived in Bethlehem of Judah, I
      and my father. They were hard times then
      in Israel, when hordes of raiding Midianites
      trampled the growing corn, burnt the young vines,
      in revenge for what they saw as our invasion
      of their land. I do not understand
      the politics; but I remember when,
      one year, in spite of careful husbandry,
      my father lost all we had sown and tended.

He had to sell his livestock: sheep, goats
      and donkeys. All he had left was me.

And in time, I too was sold. To a priest,
      a man of goodly family, who paid enough
      to secure me as a slave - but gave not quite
      enough for a bride-price. I left
      my father with regret, but found in my
      new master one who became my joy.

I thought the world of him.

But not of his cold country! Up
      in the hills of Ephraim the wind was chill

and rain was frequent. People huddled,
their faces tight against the elements.

They hammered at our door for warmth and shelter.

That door was strongly made, and I was glad
when it shut firm against the wind and cold,
and we were safe within. But though my master
treated me well, with cool and distant kindness,
I could not stay. My body longed for warmth
and sun; my heart yearned for home and father.

And so I ran away! Attached myself to a caravan
of spice merchants and travelled south with them.

My father was pleased to see me. With my slave-price
he had re-stocked the farm, and, given peace
for a time, he had begun to flourish.

And then the day that turned my life toward
its end: my master came - seeking me,
and wanting my return. Now why?

My father joked he had not known my cooking
could be so appreciated. But did this man
harbour some feeling for me? I did not dare
to hope. We exercised our hospitality,
father and I, for two-three days, both wanting
me to remain; but no! my man was bent
on taking the long trek back to Ephraim.

It was late when we began the journey;
later still coming to Jebustown
(now called Jerusalem).

We would not stop there, he said; it was not
    an Israelite town. So we pushed on, and came
    dark in an evening to Gibeah, a place
    in Benjamite country. As was the custom
    we waited in the market-square, hoping
    for rest and shelter - but no-one took us in.

There was an air of hostility about the place,
    and several boys and youths catcalled, jeered,
    and leered at me. At length an old man came
    home from work in the fields - he was from Ephraim -
    but had settled himself here in Gibeah.

He took us to his house, and I was glad
    to see it had a stout and well-made door
    for keeping out the weather.

The old man's house was warm, as was our welcome,
    and he provided well for us.
                But in the street
    the noise of drunken revels came disturbing
    our quiet rest. Hammerings on the door;
    shouted obscenities demanding that our host
    send out my man to them - to join their
    so-called fun. Which was nothing more
    than abuse and outrage, and our old host
    went out to plead with them against intended
    wickedness.

        And told them they could have -
    me - to do with as they liked.

            My heart

leaped to my mouth with fear. But surely
my master would not let them ... would not give ...

The men of Benjamin - drunk and wild
        refused to listen to the old man's pleas.

It was my master's hands which seized and pushed
        me out the door to them.

And slammed it shut - behind me.

And it was then that my heart died.

I had thought he loved me. But the door
        was shut against me - I was faced
        with a howling mob who yelled with devilish glee.

What happened to my body as they grabbed and bruised,
        raped and abused me all that night, was nothing
        to the pain of that betrayal

When morning came, I dragged my bleeding limbs
        back to the door, and held on to its threshold.

As from a distant place I saw him come,
        my master whom I had so loved.

He nearly fell - over my prostrate body.

I heard him tell me to get up, we must
        . be going.

                But my soul was being carried
        up and away - I saw him growing small

and distant.

He took his revenge on the men of Benjamin
for what they had done to me. And they
were punished, so that Israel nearly lost
one tribe out of the twelve.

But whose
were the hands that gave me to them? Who betrayed
my love and loyalty? Whose was the sin
that only thought of saving his own skin
at the expense of another's life?

There is an answer here in heaven. God
Himself has told me what it is.

Throughout our history often One must suffer
to bring truth home to any who will heed.

HANNAH
The First Book of Samuel

The shame grew slowly with the passing years,
so that, from cheerful childhood, growing up
in family warmth and love, a house resounding
with song and laughter: I became silent,
and sad.

But let me start at the beginning.
My name is Grace [5]. After five sons, my father

---

[5] "Hannah" means "grace".

was delighted, and my brothers made
much of me. My mother taught me well
her household skills, and happily encouraged
my gift of music; playing on the lyre.

There was a certain man from Ramathaim,
a Zuphite, named Elkanah-ben-Jehoram.
My father thought him suitable, and I
was more than happy in his choice for me.

At my wedding feast, my brothers sang
the song Rebekkah's brothers wished for her:
"You are our sister; may you be the mother
of many children, and may your sons possess
the cities of their enemies".

                    So the years
have passed. And I have been exemplary,
I think, in carrying out the duties of a wife.
I have done everything to make his life
easy and pleasant - except this one.
We have no children.

         So today,
Elkanah is bringing home another bride.

      *   *   *   *   *

Every year we make a pilgrimage
to Shiloh, where the priest of Adonai
makes sacrifice on our behalf. Each year,
I hope that God will hear my many prayers
and grant me sons. Peninah now has two
sons and two daughters, and her whispered taunts

disturb my heart and mind.

What have I done,
Lord God, to be thus childless? Show me my sin
that I may truly turn from it!

In anguish
I have slipped out from the feast. I cannot
eat or sleep ... Eli the priest
found me in the shadows of the temple,

silently pouring out my pleas and promises
to the Lord God of Israel. He thought
me drunk! But when I told my grief,
he blessed me, and added holy prayers
to mine.

Back home in Ramah, waiting, daring
to hope, and then rejoicing in certainty.

*   *   *   *   *

I have named him Samuel, because I asked
the Lord for him. For these five years
my husband and the family have made
the annual pilgrimage without me.
This is our time together - Samuel's
and mine.

I have taught him songs and stories;
heard his first prayers; instructed him to listen
for the Lord. And so this year he will
become God's servant. For ever. As I promised.

Peninah is curious: having waited
so long for him, how can I give him up?
Not easily! That first year was hard,
longing for childish arms around me, longing
to hear his gurgling laughter and his voice
calling for me. Hoping he wasn't lonely,
or afraid.

But in that year
I came to know contentment, and a kind
of peace.

My heart exults in God! My song
is one of triumph! I hold my head up high!
God champions the weak, the low, the poor,
and those of humble heart; while the proud
are brought down from their arrogance!
She who was childless now has many sons;
the mother of seven languishes in pain.

I have given my firstborn son back to the Lord,
and He has taken care for me with sons
and daughters. Blessed is His Name!

JEZEBEL
The Books of Kings

I, Jezebel of Israel, write.
These will become the annals of a Queen.

This was the day that saw the celebration:

my royal marriage to Ahab, Prince and Heir
Of Omri's land. It was a pact, a seal
of friendship made between Omri the Great,
his father, and Ethbaal, my father, Lord
and King of the Sidonians.

I was married
in royal purple, dye of the murex-snail,
the trademark of our land. Twelve maids
of noble birth attended me, attired
as I was, with ornaments of gold.
Ashbaal, high priest of Baal and Anathoth
joined our two hands and wound the marriage cloth
round both our bodies, closely clasped as one.

That morning, as dawn broke over the rounded
towers of Zidon city, in the white temple
by the sea, blue in the early sun,
I dedicated my life to Anath [6] - goddess
of war and love, consort and queen to Baal.
As she had done, so too would I: fight
for my lord the King; as she had brought
her husband joy in love, so too would I;
and in her honour spread the lordly names
and worship of the Baalim throughout
the land I soon would rule as Queen.

*   *   *   *   *

---

[6] In the Baal cycle of stories about the Canaanite gods, the consort of
Baal is variously known as "Anath", "Anathoth" or "Ashtoreth'. In the
Hebrew Bible she is referred to as "Asherah". Her names have been used
interchangeably here.

By the stars of Anath-Asherah, these Jews
are awkward, thick and argumentative!

In this, the fifth year of our reign, there came
this filthy, shaggy man - a Tishbeite,
who dared to threaten us - the King and Queen!
with drought and famine through the land. No rain
or dew, he said, except at his command.

His command? Is it not Baal, the lord
of heaven, who with his fecund lady Anathoth,
fights and defeats the gods of death, and thus
ensures the rain and soil fertility? This man -
Elijah, is it? - claims to speak for One
Supreme (so-called) and all-creating God,
Who goes by many names - or none.

I find that hard to believe!
                    As though any
Deity would use so rough a mouthpiece!

Well, we shall see whether our procreative
rites to Baal and Asherah defeat
the word of this mangy unkempt prophet.

          *   *   *   *   *

Three years now. The land is dry and parched.
And yet I have fulfilled my oath to Anath:
the life-blood of many prophets of this God
has been poured out for her. Yet I suspect
some have been hidden from me.

My lord and King
rides out today to seek for water in hidden
springs.

* * * * *

They have met. Ahab and Elijah.
And I have heard this troubler's doings
On Mount Carmel. How he called down the fire
from his Nameless God, and then destroyed
my prophets. A messenger from Ahab brought
the news, here to our palace in Samaria.
The man of course was killed.

As I will kill
Elijah - I swear by all the gods
of the Baalim, and by my own warlike
goddess, the Anath-Asherah. May they
deal so with me if by tomorrow he is not
as dead as one of my own men!

* * * * *

The years have passed.
I have not forgotten my old enemy
the coward Elijah. Drunk with the spirit
of his own God he braved my prophets; faced
with my anger, he fled into the hills!
But I can bide my time.

Meanwhile,
we have had some success. Our princess-daughter
Athaliah married to Jehoram,
prince of Judah. My King contended

with seige and warfare, but came safely through,
thanks be to Baal!

Now the King sulks
like a spoiled child because he cannot have
this vineyard. Who is this fellow Naboth,
who dares to thwart the wishes of a king?

Surely the King can simply take what he
desires? I shall never understand
the laws of this strange nation.

So I must
busy myself with machinations! I,
the Queen must act. And stoop to grease
the palms of scoundrels to procure the death
of Naboth ...

It is done. But are we left in peace
to enjoy our victory? I have no patience,
no respect for Ahab - mourning in sacks
and ashes, simply because that hairy prophet
spoke of disasters. Elijah haunts me still!
I burn for his end.

Grant me this
at least, my Baal, so I shall know your power
over this Nameless God!

I will not let
myself be weakened or afraid by prophecies
of my death. Though I lose all -
husband, prophets, sons - yet to the end
I will be - Jezebel of Israel!

*   *   *   *   *

I, Mehetebel, wife of Jehu,
King of Israel, complete these annals of
the Queen.

When my husband,
commander of the army, was anointed
by order of Elisha, he swept away
all that had been of Baal: princes,
and prophets; altars, temples, statues,
standing stones - all were destroyed.

Jezebel,
old, sad, embittered, but fearless to the last,
painted her face and dressed her hair and looked
out from her window - and taunted him.
She stared death in the face, and made no sound
as she was thrown - down from her high tower.

And in that moment, did she come
face-to-face with the One God she all
her life most strenuously denied?
Elijah's prophecies concerning her
came true.

When Jehu, King of Israel sent
to give her decent burial, befitting
a King's daughter, nothing was left,
but skull and hands and feet. Her body had
been eaten by wild dogs.

Thus on the plot

of land that had been Naboth's vineyard,
Jezebel met her end - and Israel's God.

THE WIDOW AT ZAREPHATH
The Book of Kings

I cannot say he trespassed on my hospitality - although
We were a self-contained togetherness, my son and I.
Together we had faced the death of man and father;
Together scraped a life of gleanings - corn and olives,
Fruit and firewood. Trying to repay our neighbours' kindnesses
With a little work.

      And then - he came.
           Elijah.

Striding the desert; shaggy coat and bearded, like a bear.
And yet his eyes were gentle, as his voice. And he was gaunt,
As we were, living at subsistence level.
Water, he wanted, and bread.
Little enough of water he could share - but bread!
Hunger sharpened my tongue; I had just enough, I swore,
To share a last meal with my son and die.

So why did I believe his crazy words? My little crock of flour
And jar of oil to be forever full? Still, I let him share our
Last cakes - after all when death is certain, does it matter if
There is less to eat? It only means the time foreshortened.

Except - I am still here.
           And so is he.

Importuning his God on my behalf for my dead boy. If I'm

Supposed to be grateful for those extra days of life, only
To have him snatched by fever, shaking his wasted limbs,
To leave me nothing - not that I asked for any reward -
(And grief is scattering my thoughts, making me incoherent)
For sheltering a man of God ...

I have been
Reviewing my sins, sitting here alone. Those
I was driven to by hunger and necessity.
Those I committed out of envy. Those I thought
About the gods: cruel and mindless, stony-faced,
Death-dealing Baalim.

Until Elijah came with words of God;
Living, life-giving, One-and-Only, Maker of earth,
Sun, moon and stars. Still, why should I believe
All that?

Unless my boy came back; unless He,
God - could show Himself powerful enough to conquer
Death itself.
Then I will believe.

VASHTI - and ESTHER
The Books of Esther

Pass me my mirror. Please.
I'm sorry; I forget I am no longer
Queen, and must request where once I could
command. Thank you. Ah yes,
this beauty holds a little, not too much.
Well, less than I would wish but rather more
than I perhaps deserve.

Is it Spring outside?
Strange how the ancient earth renews itself
ever and beautifully young each Spring,
while I, the one-time, springtime Queen to Xerxes,[7]
Harvest King, must ever fade into
perpetual winter. While Esther, young
as the morning, dew-eyed and slender,
takes my place, from foremost Concubine
to Queen.

I do not envy her. Make no mistake:
I only wish her well. She will need
all her wits, her beauty, talents
of music, song and sparkling conversation
to keep the King amused. I know; I had
some years of it - and breeding sons,
heirs to his many kingdoms; daughters
to trade for titles and to use to bargain
for foreign marriage alliances.

Do you
remember the palace garden, that paradise
of flowers and fountains, pillars, marble walks;
the hangings of white and blue and purple, echoing
the colours of sky and water and purple iris
fringing my favourite pool?

Remember too
one week of feasts? Princes, Ambassadors,

---

[7] In the two books of Esther (one in Hebrew/Aramaic; the other in Greek) the King's name appears either as Ahasuerus or Xerxes depending on the language being used. His Persian name was probably Kshayarsha.

Generals and Leaders all to be entertained
in a full riot of orgiastic splendour. Ugh!
Ahasuerus high-flown with wine - remember his command
to have me summoned, brought to be displayed.

And I had had enough. I disobeyed!
Refused to subject myself - the Queen - to all
those leering, peering eyes.

Dear me!
What a kerfuffle of legal argument!
I was a source of discord; held to be
potentially responsible for all

women's ensuing rebellion; and the cause
of every marital disharmony!
It kept the lawyers busy for a year
drawing up edicts; and gave my King
a wonderful excuse to trade me in.

My combs, if you will, and perfumes.
Old beauty habits it seems die hard
to one whose only raison d'etre was
to maintain appearances.

Mehuman, Biztha,
I thank you well for your continuing love
and loyalty - can I command yet more?
To bring me news of Esther? I would bend
such power and thought I have on her behalf,
and for her people. Do not look surprised,
I know, have always known, more than you think.

What news? What? Haman to rise to power?
That xenophobic Agagite? That snake,
devious but oh-so-clever. He will insist
on fulsome honours.

And, oh yes,
I can imagine - Mordecai, the Jew,
the new Queen's uncle, will never bow the knee
to any but the Sovereign Only-God
that he believes in.

Hmm. I foresee
a buzzing nest of trouble for the Queen.
Either she denies her race and origin
or else casts all on Xerxes' unreliable
love. Be careful Esther! Lady,
consider well! Biztha, go to her,
tell her the risks she runs by making known
what has till now been hidden.

Oh, they
are loyal these Jews! Or else stiff-necked and proud,
refusing to compromise their faith in God
and in His Laws. They should not be surprised
when tides of irrational feelings rise against
the bulwark of their creed, to throw them down.

So Haman plans mass murder? - Did I not say
it was inevitable? And Esther goes
to plead before the King; to cast
her lot with her own people and to die
as they will die. Brave Lady!

And I, Vashti, will throw my prayers before

this Jewish God, who has all things ordained.
Or so they say.

Biztha, what news?
Your face speaks of miracles! She has
succeeded? Haman hangs,
as high as he would hang all those
who thwart his power? And Mordecai
assumes his robe of state? He will wear it
with dignity and grace.

And so, Purim. [8]
A festival to celebrate release,
in every generation. Will they then
remember me? Vashti the Queen, whose small
act of defiance on behalf of women
everywhere, set off this train of huge
events?

Thus a butterfly
flutters its jewelled wings and somewhere starts
an avalanche. I have played my part
in God's design. Esther and I can go
quietly to rest, as petals fade and fall.

---

[8] Purim, a Jewish festival, still celebrated during the 13th - 15th of the
month Adar (March). It was instigated by Mordecai and Queen Esther to mark
the deliverance of the Jewish nation from extermination by Haman. At this
festival, the book of Esther is read in synagogues.

<u>Author's profile</u>:

What difficult things these are to write!

Well, I am 59, sometimes going on 72, occasionally feeling springlike when the weather is neither too hot, nor too cold.

I have five children - two of my own; two foster-children, one stepson. All these experiences of mothering I found required very different skills.

Professionally I was a speech and language therapist, but am now retired.

I am Methodist local preacher, and before retirement was also a pastoral assistant.

Hobbies: reading is probably top of the list, followed closely by gardening, writing, music and taking walks of variable length. I dislike shopping of any kind and watch the news only from a sense of duty.

RMB

Riding
Dragons

Also by Philip M Helfaer

The Psychology of Religious Doubt

Sex and Self-Respect. The Quest for Personal Fulfillment

(www.sexandselfrespect.com)

P&V

Riding Dragons

Our Journey Through Trauma To Love, Intimacy, and the Deep Self

PHILIP M. HELFAER, PhD

VELLIE HELFAER, BSN, MSN

P&V Press
Pittsboro, North Carolina

Book cover by Monkey C Media
Interior design by Asya Blue Design, LLC

First Edition
Printed in the United States of America

ISBN. 979-8-9851775-0-3 (Trade Paperback)
ISBN: 979-8-9851775-1-0 (eBook)

Library of Congress Control Number: 2021922633

How could anyone ever tell you
you were anything less than beautiful?
How could anyone ever tell you
you were less than whole?
How could anyone fail to notice that
your loving is a miracle?
How deeply you're connected to my soul.

— Libby Roderick, *How Could Anyone* (1988)

Knowing that he did not know, Jacob begins to know.
The Zohar reads his waking speech – va-anokhi lo
yadati – "I – I did not know," as referring to his own
self-hood: "I have not known my anokhi – my self." The
emphatic I, the subject of his insight, also becomes the
object. As object of reflection, anokhi, a new awareness
of self, generates a profound sense of past ignorance.
Jacob is able to surrender to the mystery of his own
mind, to lose himself in an immediate experience: this
in itself constitutes his new awareness. For the first
time, he knows that he has never known himself, never
integrated the fragmented perspectives that so agitate
the angels.

— Avivah Gottlieb Zornberg, *The Murmuring Deep:*
Reflections on the Biblical Unconscious (2009)

Contents

Acknowledgments

We appreciate our five trusted associates who read early drafts of our book in whole or in part and offered commentary: Prof. Mary Anne Bright, Prof. Peter Fernald, Ms Susan Kanor, Ms Kathleen Spivack, and Dr. Divna Peric-Todorovic. We thank Kathleen Spivack, poet, novelist, writing coach extraordinary, and friend for her encouragement and help. We thank our "West Coast Editorial Board," Marcy Rein and Clif Ross. We thank John Fielding Walsh, prominent figure in the publishing world, for taking the time to offer friendly and generous advice. As always we are grateful to Alexander Lowen, M.D. who created the field of bioenergetic analysis and established the International Institute for Bioenergetic Analysis. Even though there was much to develop and improve upon in both the field and the institute, it gave us an organizational setting in which to learn, teach, and develop. We both benefitted from Philip's earlier mentors: Prof. Robert N. Bellah and Prof. Daniel J. Levinson in social science and Prof. Norman Malcolm in philosophy. We could not have evolved our understanding of ourselves as we did without that preliminary training.

The two epigraphs introducing the book are both meaningful for us, and we gratefully acknowledge permission for their use:

Demons and Dragons: A Dialogue

Aleph: Tav and Tava, demons and dragons are images of mythic beings from millennia past. Are you rewriting a myth?

Tava: You could say so. But our experience gave us the stories we write.

Tav: We lived through times when we were engaged with demons.

Aleph: What was it like?

Tav: I felt them. They were real enough. They tore at me, hurt me, and took my energy.

Tava: And I experienced the horrors.

Aleph: Were you frightened?

Tav: There were moments when I did not know if I would survive.

Tava: And times I wanted to die. We were in the grip of forces over which we had no control; forces that felt like they came from underground.

Aleph: Ah, so that's what was real – the forces. How did you survive?

Tav: We learned that the forces were in our underground depths; they were our demons; they were me.

Aleph: So you were living in the natural energies of your own beings that have such depth and strength.

Tav: Yes. And that's where the reality of the myths come in. The forces of nature are greater than our small selves. When we acknowledge them within ourselves, demons become dragons.

Aleph: Aren't dragons just as bad?

Tava: Dragons are different; they don't tear at you; they are known for protecting precious treasures.

Aleph: They protect you! You are what is precious, your own self.

Tav: Yes. That's why we can say we are riding dragons.

Preface

One sunny warm day in October 1991, the clerk of the small town where we lived, Pepperell, Massachusetts, came to our home and officiated at our marriage. At that time, Vellie was fifty-five and Phil was fifty-eight. We had become a couple and lived together for ten years before this day. And, during the ten years before that, we were sometimes lovers, constant friends, and eventually colleagues.

We were in our mid-forties when we became a couple. Phil was born in 1933, Vellie in 1936. Both of us were raised in small towns, Vellie in the Deep South, in Louisiana, Phil in the north, in New York state, near the Great Lakes. Regardless of the geographic and cultural spread between our towns, in the 1960s, it happened that we both were in the Boston area for professional training in psychology, psychotherapy, and mental health. Our paths first converged in 1970, and as the 1970s progressed they gradually intertwined. We shared training in the same kind of psychotherapy and eventually shared a practice.

At the time we became a couple, we longed to fulfill our yearnings for sexual love with a loved partner. However, our capacity for love was undeveloped and disturbed, and this had been the case since our adolescence. Our passionate seeking to realize our wishes brought us directly into contact with the inner emotional disturbances standing in the way of fulfilling love and desire. These dominated our inner worlds. We often found ourselves in states of fear, rage, shock, and suffering. We understood these disturbances as the destructive effects of multiple, painful traumas experienced as children.

We devoted more time, attention, energy, and strenuous effort to learning to live in love and enjoyment than to anything else. This has been our way of life. Often frightened and unsure, we remained committed body and soul to our lived experience – whether joyful and exciting or deeply painful. For us, and for many others we have known, such is the path to love and fulfillment with another person.

We are proud of the work we have done. We accepted the sometimes agonizing struggles to sort out our sexualities. We often did not know the way, but we stayed the course. And we were able to remain dedicated to our goals, free ourselves from inner disturbance, remain connected, and find a safe haven, peace, love, and well being within ourselves and in our connection with each other.

Several years ago, when we looked back, we were excited about the lengthy process that brought us to this happy time. At this point, I (Phil) was moved to start writing about my experience. I did not make a plan. I knew I wanted to write about the outstanding graphic mental and emotional pictures that had emerged in my mind over the preceding years. Each of the depictions I wrote captured some kernel of the essence of my life. Eventually these depictions became chapters with headings and subheadings, interrelated through emotion and an emerging sense of my identity.

After reading my chapters for a year, Vellie became engaged in the same exciting process for herself. She found self-affirmation in her skills and intuition. Now we read each other's chapters and shared our experiences in intimate, feelingful ways.

Our series of chapters cover the most significant aspects of our developmental years up to adulthood, our adult years before we became a couple, and the crucial developments and changes that occurred after we became a couple. Themes include the difficult struggles around sexual identity and expression, our capacity for being with another person, and our capacity for surviving in the social world. They are explorations of the inner worlds underlying our difficulties, descriptions of how we went about freeing ourselves, and above all, the process of finding ourselves and our capacity for love.

We have one goal or intention that makes publication important for us. Our reports (as we call them) challenge a set of boundaries, and it is our intention to challenge them. The boundaries have to do with recognition of the life of the deeper self, the inner life of the individual.

These boundaries have to do with selfhood. When we explored our inner selves and troublesome behaviors coming from them, we encountered shame, humiliation, fear, and negative self-evaluation. These affects are the way these boundaries function. They regulate, suppress, censor, hide, and protect all aspects of inner experience. Exploring these emotions and their roots in the safety and privacy of our relationship and our home is enriching and leads to change and inner strengthening.

Through our efforts, we freed ourselves personally of much of our anxiety and shame passed on from the culture of our families. But our culture in fact does still retain the same or similar boundaries in the forms of judgments and disapprobation that affected us in the first place. When we share our reports publicly, we are exposed once again to the action of these boundaries.

And here is where we protest! We protest against forms of social mores that caused us unnecessary harm and suffering. We want to shift social mores to allow for the healthy, freer, development of the inner life and the expression of feeling, excitement, curiosity, and the meeting of natural needs. We want to do what little we can to challenge the cultural envelope and move it towards the awareness and acceptance of a wider range of life experience. Our belief is that social mores regarding the development of the self are best when guided by love and an understanding of health. We believe this is the most basic way to enrich human life.

Our reports define and demonstrate the practice of self-study. We believe it is a crucial way to open the boundaries of the cultural and social mores that constrain and impair development of the individual person. The practice of self-study could have a place in the cultural and social world, and it could be a part of daily life. It could be understood as an aspect of education and child development that leads to a healthier, more resilient adult who is capable of empathy and love. Self-study as a practice neutralizes the almost universal tendency to turn the other into the bad or evil other. Self-study is the practice that allows us to own and take responsibility for our negative attitudes in the way that strengthens the self. It allows room for the development of self-love, thus enhancing the capacity to love others.

We hope readers will find that our reports touch on themes intimately concerning their lives and that they will stimulate reflection. More importantly we wish that they will encourage and support others in their own unique journeys to develop the capacity for love and intimacy and to discover their deeper self. To these people we dedicate this book.

Philip M. Helfaer, PhD
Vellie Helfaer, BSN, MSN
Summer 2021

PART I

Phil

Wisdom is the realization that life is a journey, the meaning of which is found in the voyage and not in the destination.

– Alexander Lowen, *Fear of Life* (1980)

CHAPTER 1

"You May"

Boston 1970: A Journey Begins

The moment remains with me as distinct as a sharply drawn etching. Vellie opened her apartment door, and we glimpsed each other for the first time. There was a brief silence while the space between us lit up and came alive with curiosity and excitement. Her expression struck me. I could not read it, and I never did find words for it. But it was genuine, alive, and it must have been expressing warmth and excitement, because I found myself immediately (and guiltily) having sexual ideas.

A mutual friend had urged us to meet. Eventually I called Vellie and invited her to dinner. I do not remember going out to eat and talking, although I know that we did, and I know that she accepted my invitation to come home with me.

We were on the sofa kissing and getting to know each other when, without coyness or pretense, Vellie said, "You may." Her meaning was perfectly clear. Spoken in her soft, gentle voice, never had two words been more endearing.

Soon we were together in my candlelit bedroom. The beauty of her slender swimmer's body and the pleasure of our lovemaking spread through me, leaving an enduring impression.

Both of us were in ongoing relationships, but from time to time in those first years, we wanted each other and looked forward to the relaxed pleasure of our lovemaking. We met for supper at the Red Fez, a Near Eastern restaurant in a drab Boston neighborhood, where we ordered salad and lamb with green beans. By the end of the meal, we impatiently hurried back to my apartment.

I still lived in rundown graduate student digs in Somerville on the other side of the Charles River. We were entirely happy there. Occasionally we managed a weekend hiking or skiing in New Hampshire. We talked easily – about ourselves, our relationships, our work – and we made love.

Vellie stayed with her man. In my relationship, I was troubled, and I separated in a cloud of confusion and suffering. Less than a year later I was with another woman, and I told Vellie that I had to give up our sexual relationship. We stayed friends, became colleagues, and shared office space. When another colleague and I initiated a study group, Vellie joined.

I always welcomed her warm companionship. As office mates and friends, we studied psychotherapy, talked about cases, and attended experiential workshops together. One of these concluded with the offer of the sensual experience of a "sweat lodge." While several of us stood around – naked – waiting our turns, Vellie showed up next to me, also naked. My erection quickly revealed that my feelings for her were still alive. Discreet as she is, she tried to shield me.

A Shaky Guy

As to marriage, Vellie and I were not just late bloomers; so far, these particular "blooms" had not sprung forth, even though we both, consistently and constantly, lived in one or another long-term relationship. In time, the inevitable happened. Ten years after our first meeting, we found ourselves unattached at the same time. Vellie was forty-three and I was forty-six. One day during this coincidence of our singularities, we met in Vellie's apartment to make plans for new office space. We finished with our business, and I went home.

Vellie called later that day.

She said, "What was going on at lunch? Did you feel it? I was excited. Can you come in tonight? Or plan to get together after work tomorrow?"

"Well ... " I hesitated, and then I said, "I'll get some stuff together and drive in."

Back with Vellie, we first asked, "What are we going to do with each other?" Then we concluded with the obvious, "We don't know what we are going to do with each other." After that, I gratefully gave in to our familiar affection and the pleasure and ease of our lovemaking.

The evening Vellie invited me back to her apartment I was grieving the loss of the woman with whom I had a close sexual relationship for several years. I felt awful. Vellie knew I was feeling shaky, although she did not know just how shaky.

This ending was not the first of its kind. There had been others, and I had dropped opportunities for promising beginnings. I could not imagine being married and having children. Inevitably the aftermath of these endings gave rise to painful loneliness, self-doubting anxiety, and suffering. My age now pointed to worrisome questions. Was this my fate – always to leave or be left? Would something so ordinary as an enduring relationship elude me for the rest of my life? Pain and suffering pervaded me, far beyond the sadness of the loss itself.

A Vow

A stark image remains with me from the time following that separation.

I am walking down Dana Street towards Mass Avenue having just left the safety of the psychotherapy office Vellie and I shared. I can't imagine feeling worse than I did at that moment. I dreaded being seen by anyone I knew. A woman passes me. I surreptitiously glance at her to see if she notices a creature less than human. I can feel my scowl, the tension in my face. I walk past the corner restaurant. Out of the corner of my eye I notice an acquaintance at the table by the window. I grip and walk on.

Within me, desperation and dread rose from terrible convictions about myself that usually lay coiled, like a snake, at the dark bottom of the pit of my self.[1] *There must be something horribly wrong about my sexual needs.*

My desperation yielded one good thing. I understood I had to do something about myself. *I had to do something different.* In this frightened state, I made a vow to myself, sacred as if from Zion. *The next time (if there were a next time) I find myself in the kind of close, sexual relationship, like those I had ended – this time, come hell or high water, I will not end it. I will stay the course. I will commit myself. I will stay with her if she will have me, and she will be the one, and with her I will learn to love and be loved.*

Vellie's call dropped like a seed from Eve's ripe apple into the torn-up ground of my heart and soul. Flourishing and

---

1 See Glossary, "myself vs. my self."

blooming were doubtful. In my vulnerable state, my newly minted vow untested, the merest possibility of even one night together aroused more anxiety than desire. I was frightened that night when I returned to be with Vellie, and at that time, I had no way to communicate my feeling. But I also felt lonely and undesirable, and with Vellie, I felt safe and wanted. Happily, my fear did not overwhelm my sexual pleasure and the warmth of our connection.

Changes

We changed, both of us, right from the start. Vellie discovered that her "steady date" model of having a man for weekend companionship no longer applied. It seemed that she, at age forty-three, was asking what happened to the vague plans for marriage and family that she had never relinquished but that had never materialized. Now our being together mattered to her in a new kind of way. She wanted it. She felt more in every way. For myself, the sharpest of the pain dissipated, and I came back to a semblance of my whole self. Anxious stress and dark shades were never too far away, but I once again felt the pulsing stream of life and pleasure.

We did not make a commitment then and there, nor did we come to a decision in the next few weeks. But over the next several months, step by small step, we allowed ourselves to give in to accepting our affection and need for each other. And those steps moved steadily on over the next two or three years.

We spent nights after work in her apartment, and on Saturday she would drive out to my house. We might have a champagne lunch. We began to share our anxieties and difficulties. We were filled with multitudes of feelings, some wonderful and exciting, some disturbing and painful.

An Ominous Harbinger

Not long after our new beginning, we met two colleague-friends for supper at a restaurant near Harvard Square. We all knew each other from weekly meetings of our psychotherapy study group, and we chatted familiarly as we dallied over a dessert menu. I dropped some silly remark expressing my hesitancy about being a "piggy." Vellie observed that "Piggy" was fond of chocolate desserts.

I erupted.

Out of me came a violent, cruel, verbal attack on Vellie. It burst out of me with no deliberation. Our friends sat in shocked silence. Vellie looked down and said nothing. My shame and horror at myself were immediate. I have no memory of what I said.

To this day, my heart sinks when I remember that moment. Vellie asked herself many times why and how it was that she stayed with me. Yet she did, and we remained together.

Hidden Realities

The excitement and promise that sparked between us the first time we met – what of that?

With the prospect of being together as a couple, all kinds of feelings surfaced in her and in me. The denser texture of our connection fueled my anxiety.

When Vellie playfully addressed "Piggy," she leaned towards me and, in her soft voice, spoke to me in tones of warm intimacy. I reacted as if she were showing everyone and reminding me that we were a couple, as if we were married. This mere hint awakened in me the keen fear and rage that had torn apart my relationships with other women. At the restaurant that evening, I might have been subliminally aware of what set me off, but blind forces drove me. Between Vellie's sweet intimacies and my outburst, there was barely a fraction of a second.

Dual Traumas

My outburst of fear and rage was driven by hidden inner realities, disturbances, traumas, and pain from childhood. Vellie's history and mine had much in common. Now, being together as a couple doubled the energy of emotions associated with past hurts: rage, terror, fear, horror, and the humiliation, shame, and self-hate associated with emotional and sexual abuse and neglect.

Our vulnerabilities left us sensitized and hyperreactive, generating episodes of quarreling and distress. We made painful attempts to resolve each episode. We sat facing each other: me in my rocking chair, both of us tense and stirred up. Vellie is more than reluctant to talk and for good reason. I insist that she face up to her "provocation" and "understand" what made me go bonkers this time. She does her best to protect herself, not only from me, but even more, from her own tendency to fall into abysmal guilt, assuming that, once again, it is all her fault.

We sit, each in our own aloneness and unhappiness. Vellie becomes a stranger whose intentions I distrust. My heart is drained of empathy. Vellie feels the awful effects of being regarded with anger and love gone cold. Often, I'm in a state of shock, my eyes want to close, and I can hardly stay awake. Vellie, too, goes into shock, freezes, and repeatedly says, "I don't know."

Some days pass in a standoff; we quiet down. I soften and relent enough to drop my grievances. The hurt in our hearts diminishes, and we ease back into connection. Closeness and affection return. Once again I acknowledge to myself that in my heart I know that Vellie is not the source of my suffering. On the contrary, once again her stalwart spirit protected me from being stuck in the darkness of my own soul.

Guidance from a Wise Teacher

We told ourselves that "our maturity and understanding will guide us in storms and rough waters, and at the same time, we can help one another." These sentiments had merit, but they did not take into account our hidden inner realities.

We love Martin Buber's words:

> The essential thing is to begin with oneself ... there is no way out but by the crucial realization: Everything depends on myself, and the crucial decision: I will straighten myself out ... [H]e must find his way ... to his own self: he must find his own self ... the deeper self of the person living in a relationship to the world. And that is also contrary to everything we are accustomed to.[2]

He spoke in truth. We were not "accustomed." I understood the importance of the "crucial decision," but my understanding had not ripened into a capacity to hold me consistently to its purpose. At moments of crisis, I failed to be grounded in a commitment to "straighten myself out."

Despite my experience and understanding, when Vellie and I became a couple, I wasn't developed enough to find my way to my deeper self, as Buber taught, or of course, to find the way to the love I longed for. In the actuality of our everyday life, I protected the hurt part of myself in a way that weakened my ability and even my willingness to abide by Buber's teaching. Instead, I vociferously claimed the prerogative of staking out positions and dealing self-justifying arguments. I based my claims on the unspoken but clearly communicated belief that she, the other, was the source of the distress, and she needed to

2 Martin Buber, *The Way of Man: According to the Teaching of Hasidism* (New York: Citadel Press, 1966), pp. 29–30.

reform herself. These bitter fandangos hurt us. Our inner injuries flared, burnt out, and left the ashes of aloneness, sorrow, heartache, and feeling the unfairness of suffering for love.[3]

Self-Study and Its Methods

From the beginning, we poured our energies into liberating our love for each other and realizing the good we knew was in us. We made this work the center of our lives. We saw it as a journey we were on together and as our healing path. We felt pride in taking it on and in the experience and knowledge that we brought to bear on it.

When we became more focused, we called what we were doing *self-study* and *self-development*. We were equipped with practices that facilitated our work. As therapists we worked with bioenergetic analysis, a therapy based on direct work with the body. We talked. We wrote in our journals. We used psychedelic substances and marijuana.

In the face of repeated overwhelming experiences, with the aid of our self-study practices, we sustained our connection. Time and again, my upset and anger calmed down, and the storm passed through. Once again, I grasped that my chaos of hurt, rage, guilt, fear of loss, and desperation was a terrible state left in my body and nervous system from childhood. Amazingly, my love for Vellie returned. Gratefully I again felt the dear closeness with her, and I could not fathom how it was that I could ever feel anything different. I felt our bond of love and care, and I held her to me. I trusted this bond, I depended on it, and neither she nor I ever let it be challenged for long.

---

3 Notice that throughout we are referring to emotional suffering. We are not comparing our experience with the suffering of peoples in war zones, refugees, or people who suffer with terrible illness, or from any other kind of catastrophic life trauma.

CHAPTER 2

The Tunnel of Time

Home! A complicated concept.

– Kathleen Spivack, *Unspeakable Things* (1981)

Night Vision on Happy Meadows

We left Massachusetts in March 2013 and migrated to North Carolina where we built a solar house. We named our new home "Happy Meadows." It lies in the North Carolina piedmont, in the middle of the state. We live here in loving affection, without the duress of earlier years.

We were ready to settle down. We had taken on teaching in Norway and Israel that required travel every year. Our Norway connection was fifteen years, and with Israel it was twenty years. For the last twelve of those we lived in Israel.

One night after we had been at Happy Meadows for a year or so, I awoke and sat on the edge of our bed enjoying the darkness, the quiet, and my state of mind. Vellie slept peacefully, her breathing soft. An image emerged.

I felt our years had passed as if time itself were a kind of gigantic tunnel through which we had hurtled, swept along in a rumpus of primal elements. After many stormy years, we find ourselves deposited in the peace and quiet of our new home. Along this tumultuous, raucous passage, cruel forces threatened to tear us both into pieces and apart from each other. But Vellie and I managed to remain connected, even when our being together generated the energy for the forces that tore at us. Occasionally we dropped into a small, safe place, like a little harbor, a glade in the forest, or a gentle, sunny mountain slope, and for a moment, we enjoyed the beauty around us.

In this vision, I also see my passage through time as a psychologist, a professional person. When I began practice years ago – and all along for most of the following years – I knew little about my own archaic soul, and it is just this I most needed to study. Inadvertently, perhaps, but insistently and early on, this is what I set about doing.

Here, now, in our peaceful place, this is the gift that the passage of time in all its storms and meanderings has bestowed upon me: becoming acquainted with and understanding my own soul, evolving a fullness of my being that enables my capacity to love and find peace.

"Home Is Where One Starts From"[4]

In 1924, well before the economy crashed, my father took a job as a chemist at a new factory in Buffalo, New York, which manufactured dyes. My brother, nearly ten years older than me, had already been born that year, in Madison, Wisconsin; my sister, seven years older, was born in Buffalo.

My father preferred small-town living to the city, and before I was born, he moved his young family to a village with

4 T. S. Eliot, *Four Quartets*, Part II, "East Coker," V (London: Faber & Faber, 2001).

nice middle-class homes. There were no visible signs of poverty, and there were no people of color in the village – or in the schools I went to – for the whole time I lived there. There were, perhaps, four or five Jewish families, of which ours was one. Our village, Hamburg, is fifteen miles south of where my father's factory used to be.

The tiny point when I entered the tunnel of time in this village goes back to 1933. A few years after my birth, my father's income allowed him to install his family in an attractive house on a lovely tree-lined street. I was three when we moved, my sister ten, and my brother thirteen. From the time I can remember until I finished college, home was that house, street, and village, and in nostalgic memory, it remained home for many years.

I had specific sensual feelings for every corner, nook, and cranny of the house, from the attic that could be entered only by bringing up a ladder, to the strange, dark crawl space – a hole in the wall in the cellar filled with old boards from when the house was built. The one room that had a cold, uninhabited feeling for me was the "living room," which was not at all a living room. It was the formal room, used when my parents had guests. It had more expensive furniture, nice wallpaper, and various vases that Mother bought from time to time. The one good thing about it was the fireplace, where occasionally we built a log fire. The "sunroom" was the informal, comfortable room where I would read, and there were the upstairs bedrooms: my parents', one I shared with my brother, and one that was my sister's.

Our house sat on a roomy lot. Two old tulip trees with massive columnar trunks stood guard at the front sidewalk. Way in the back, an old dirt tennis court, long gone to desuetude, extended an already lengthy back yard past rusting twelve-foot fencing. My interest focused on an odd little fishpond in a nook in the middle of the west side of the yard. Mother's "rock garden" surrounded it, and an old plum tree, which scattered little rotting fruits in the summer, and an old, gnarled apple tree, which bore no apples, shaded opposite sides of the pond. I enjoyed climbing in these unusual, cranky old trees. A few little goldfish who gave the tiny pond its name survived for a surprising length of time, given the neglect they endured.

A five-minute trek through our back yard and then the neighbor's, took me to my "crick," the Eighteen Mile Creek. My approach brought me to the top of a slope from where I looked down at the creek bed; a giant willow tree with multiple trunks growing at its edge. A low shale cliff jutted up on the opposite side. Many days I wandered and explored in this little landscape, and from it a sense of being a part of the natural world infused my spirit as I grew.

Home Life

I did not feel actively engaged with my parents. After I was five or six, I have very few memories of talking with either of them. I spent hardly a moment with my mother, but every now and then I would experience a companionable time with my father. Even with the emotional and cultural barrenness, I felt safe and comfortable at home. Both of my parents were quiet and steady. My trust that my father would provide for us was unquestioned. And despite her chronic stresses, my mother was just as steady in keeping up our home and providing meals.

My father was my favorite parent. His morning routine on weekdays is one of my clearest impressions of him. From the time I remember, he carpooled to work with two or three other men from our town. He rushed through the breakfast he made for himself (mother was still in bed), then, coffee cup in hand, charged up and ready for work, he stood watch at the front window waiting for his ride.

My father commuted and worked with these men, and a few others from our town, for many years. He had his own life with them and with his management of the factory, which was entirely separate from his home life. He was a hard worker, a serious person and very competent. His investment in his job must have been considerable, and perhaps it outweighed his involvement with his house, wife, and relationships with his kids. At home, he was quiet, and his sharing of household life with my mother was limited. He had his sphere and she hers.

In my imagination, going to the factory in Buffalo day in and day out was something unpleasant and dreary that took a lot of strength to endure. It was in a gritty, coal-blackened area, open-hearth iron mills belched fire and smoke to the south, and the roughest part of the city lay just to the north. A small door admitted workers into the factory, and I had little idea of what went on behind a dirty brick facade.

I admired his calm, sturdy manner. Now and then, I'd say, "Make a muscle," and he'd flex a muscular arm. To me, he looked like a father and a man should look, and he acted accordingly. He held himself with down-to-earth self-respect, but his demeanor had a tough edge that said, "I mean business. No slacking off."

So it was that I absorbed from him the unrelenting expectation that continuous, steady – mostly joyless – work is the core of life, what a man must do. The need to live up to him drove me. But I lived in uncertainty as to whether I worked hard enough or whether the work I did do was of a sort that counted anyway. He never indicated one way or another.

Eagerly, as a little boy, I awaited his return in the evening. He arrived home at six o'clock, placidly received my excitement that he was home and greeted my mother in the kitchen with a perfunctory kiss. Mother never failed to have supper waiting. Her meals were simple, but carefully planned and prepared. She was thoughtful about nutrition and meals always involved meat, potato and another vegetable. Everything was cooked in the plainest way; there were no "dishes" or sauces from cookbooks. She often put out a salad, usually no more than part of a head of lettuce. My father referred to it as "bunny food."

After going upstairs to wash, he descended to supper in the dining room. Still wearing his shirt, suspenders, and tie, he presided, as tradition called for, at the head of the table where he would cut up and serve the meat. He relaxed after supper, sometimes with a brief nap, and then he would usually read the *Buffalo Evening News* until he went to bed. In the evening, as in the morning, he rarely spoke.

While my siblings were still at home, we all ate together in the dining room. We were not a very lively family, or particularly close, but in my childhood years, we were an orderly, stable family. I drew security from this stability.

My mother, of course, referred to me as her "baby." When my siblings left home for college, I was still a child, now sort of an only child, but maybe more like an extra. I always sensed that I grew up in a sphere different from and outside that of my siblings, and my parents seemed more engaged with their sphere.

My mother managed house and home. She did not question her traditional role as housewife and mother. I remember her sitting at her little secretariat writing out checks in her beautiful script to pay bills. I remember her out in the yard, hanging the washing out to dry; in the winter she hung it in the cellar. And I remember her in the kitchen in the late afternoons preparing supper. Off and on she hired someone to come in and help her, as she did when I was a baby, but for many years she must have also taken care of daily house cleaning, changing beds, and other household chores.

She took care of Dad's clothing. Every day he wore a suit to work, and my mother had his suits made by a tailor in our village. The Blue Bird laundry regularly picked up Dad's shirts and returned them cleaned and starched. We also had our milk and dairy products delivered from the Hamburg Dairy. The milk bottles presented me with a little amusement. On one side of the bottle two babies (in diapers) said, "We want our Hamburg Dairy milk." On the other side of the bottle, they said, "We have our Hamburg Dairy milk."

I was given a few chores, but my workload was minor. Saturday morning as a boy I washed the kitchen floor while I listened to "Let's Pretend" on the radio. By high school it was my job to wash the dishes after supper. Occasionally I was sent "uptown," a walk of three or four blocks, to get groceries or go to the meat market.

In my experience of her, my mother was often suffering. She had headaches, fatigue, and colitis. I rarely saw her enjoy herself. One thing she did enjoy was beautifying her home, which she did bit by bit over the years. She was frugal about it – although not frugal enough for my father. The house furnishings and her clothing reflected her soft, feminine, aesthetic feeling for colors, textures, and beauty.

When I was a teenager and there were just myself and my parents, we continued the tradition of eating supper together, but now we ate in the kitchen. These mealtimes were uncomfortable for me, and probably for my parents. Neither of my parents were talkative, and by then I had taken my father's practice of silence to a different level. I sat at the table swinging my foot, humming to myself, off in my own world, where my adolescent sexual ruminations stayed secret, biding their time in a realm in my consciousness vague enough for me to stay comfortably preoccupied.

What Did I Do with Myself?

I was a few weeks short of twelve when the first atomic bomb was exploded over Hiroshima, ushering in the atomic era. I cautiously bought my first black and white television set when I was a graduate student in the mid-1960s. About twenty years later, I owned my first computer, an Apple McIntosh; the digital era began and flew on with dizzying speed.

My childhood and adolescence in the late 1930s and 1940s were free of the distractions of television and digital devices. I was born into the quiet life of a small town. After school and during the summer holidays, hanging out at home, I was on my own when it came to determining how I was going to use my time and direct my attention and energy. I had the opportunity to be bored and wonder what to do. I loved to immerse myself in books, especially classic literature and adventure. And I daydreamed. I was a regular inhabitant of the woods and creek. From time to time, I had pals for adventures, hiking with Gaither and his dog, Sophie, or making gunpowder with Jack, the boy in the house on the next street.

I did have a radio, and there were one or two early evening programs I tuned in to regularly, like *Jack Armstrong, the All-American Boy*, *Superman*, and *The Lone Ranger*. A Sunday evening ritual was listening to a few longer programs, like *Jack Benny*, *The Shadow*, *Blondie*, and others. This was the last fun thing to do on the weekend before the drudgery of school the next day.

In high school as a teenager, I was busy full time – in plays, editing the school paper, managing for the football team, and orchestra. At home in the evenings, I washed the dishes and did homework.

What it came to, I'd say, is that I was with myself. And that felt like the natural way to be. Being with myself allowed me to maintain contact with my feelings and natural rhythms. If I was taken out of myself, it was by a book or my own daydreams.

A Confusing Discrepancy

There is a striking discrepancy in my life and history that always puzzled me. There was the steadiness, security, calm, and quiet of my life in my family and in my village. And then there was the person I found myself to be and the life I found myself living from the day I left home. My emotional life was turbulent and painful, and effectively managing my life in the social world was a struggle.

From my family life, I took strengths and skills that allowed me to manage and survive. I also took anxiety, depression, and inner emotional disturbance, topped with a leaden hodgopodge of unrealistic expectations about what I should do and must be. These made my survival a struggle. The disturbances and negative forces at work in my family were invisible to me. My mission became bringing the hidden to light.

PART II

Vellie

CHAPTER 3

Louisiana 1936

Birth

I was born in 1936 in a small town in Louisiana, in America's Deep South. My parents finished building a new house on land that was part of my paternal grandfather's cotton farm just in time for my birth. The country family doctor and probably my grandmother were with my mother for my home birth.

My parents' first child was a boy who lived only a few hours. Two girls followed, one five years my senior and the other three years older. My being the third daughter was considered a misfortune of nearly biblical proportions. This was according to my parents' spoken and unspoken mythology, reinforced by the extended family especially on my father's side. According to family lore, a boy was wanted – and needed – to carry on the family name, the special male line of descent. And this was the last chance for my father's family, since my parents were not going to have any more children. And my father was the only son in a family with five daughters.

The family stories I heard from the time I could understand what was being said made it clear to me that my arrival prompted painful disappointment. From her stories, I picked up the impression that, in those first moments, my mother turned away from her baby. Scattered over time I heard other bits and pieces of her story revealing that she had suffered from my father's family's anger. In those days, a birth mother could be blamed for this kind of "failure."

For my father's sisters, the disappointment and sense of loss continued through the years. For one of my aunts, it was particularly important to keep the family name alive. Each time one of my sisters had a child she would tell her to use the family name as a middle name. My sisters and I would joke and laugh about this, considering her request trivial, but we felt the intensity of her determination to preserve the family name. I laughed but always felt a fleeting moment of being accused.

Nameless Baby

A feeling in my body of being the wrong one, and the one to be blamed, began at the moment of my arrival into the family and into the world. My parents' painful disappointment entered me with my mother's milk and settled into my body. Those bodily feelings affected my identity, generating bad feelings within me that carried into many of my life experiences and situations. This diminished the energy available for my healthy development.

Perhaps because my parents were so intent on having a boy, it was a week before they gave me a name. The next Sunday after my birth, my father looked in the paper and chose my name. I always felt that my father being the one to choose my name, and the way he chose it, was a gesture by my parents that expressed their wish to deny my femininity. Mother chose names for my sisters, and she frequently spoke with pride about her choices.

I told Phil I experienced my name as heavy. Later he spontaneously started calling me "Vellie," which touched my heart because it feels light. It soon became my name.

A Baby Who Needed to Be Held

The new home did not have conveniences that came later, like electricity, telephone, or indoor running water. We used kerosene lamps, and I can still picture the soft, warm glow in the evenings and my mother sitting in a rocking chair. We had large yards, a garden area, and an area for my father's beehives. I started my life in a home where we lived close to the natural world and the land, and that fact played a significant role in my development.

Without the conveniences, it was not an easy life for my mother. She must have been busy with all she had to do with a three-year-old toddler and a five-year-old who was dealing with a second displacement. But, however little time and energy she had left for a new baby, she still breastfed me for several months.

I was a "good baby," according to her story, so quiet she could forget about me. When she would eventually come to me, she found me playing with my feet, not making a sound. At about six months, I developed oral thrush, and I stopped eating. My mother struggled with my not eating, but when I started losing my hair and became even quieter, they took me to a doctor. He recommended that someone needed to hold me almost continuously and feed me with a dropper.

Depressed and exhausted, my mother needed help. Her mother and mother-in-law both came, so my mother, or one of my grandmothers, had the time to hold me for hours every day over a couple of weeks. Years later when we talked, Mother would describe the time and how I responded to being held. Evidently, I had a form of failure to thrive. Mother told me she had been depressed for the first two years of my life, and this must have affected me. I do not know if it was a clinical post-partum depression or if it was a situational deep unhappiness. Given her many difficulties, my mother gave me all she could.

Out of these early life experiences around my birth, a multilayered adaptation evolved that continued throughout my life. In a small town in Louisiana in 1936, my life began with being blamed for being born female. In my first year of life, I passed through a period of hanging between living and dying. Throughout my life, I lived with the theme "I am the wrong one." I frequently experienced the – usually hidden – wish to give up altogether. At the same time, within me I have a willful determination to be alone and take care of myself. Fortunately, these elements are balanced by my capacity to respond positively to contact and warmth.

A Child's Life on the Farm

My parents lived with my father's parents in the family house on their cotton farm for several years. Those years included the births of the boy who died and of my two sisters. For a short period, while they were building their new home, my parents managed to move out of my grandparents' house and into one of the old, small sharecropper tenant houses that was closer to their new house. Our mother told us how she tried to clean the house with lye and do what she could to make it livable for two small children. She must have been relieved to be in her own new home by the time of my birth.

Our country life left a sensuous mix of feelings in nostalgic memory. There were times in the late afternoon, after my grandparents finished with the day's work, when my sisters and I would sit with them on their broad front porch. We looked out over the large yard and the bayou with the small bridge we crossed to get to the main road. A feeling of peace and quiet held us. Our grandparents enjoyed having us with them.

I have fond memories of my mother making us small "cotton-picking bags" that hung over our shoulders, so my sisters and I could go out into the cotton field as a special treat. I was maybe four or five years old. Picking cotton is difficult, so I imagine we picked each cotton boll very carefully, trying not to hurt our little hands and fingers. To my delight, my grandfather weighed me along with my bag of cotton on a large set of scales, and he paid me accordingly. Every worker had a tobacco can for their pay, and we received our money along with them. Riding to the mill on the horse-driven wagon filled with cotton was another exciting activity. All these details remain as partial visual and physical memories: my grandfather putting me up on the scales, the tobacco can rattling with pennies, and the horse-driven wagon filled with cotton.

Less Fond Memories

One Easter, Mother spent a lot of time making me a beautiful pink coat, which I did not like (it may simply have been too hot). I was always puzzled about the story of me as a small child not liking a coat, how it felt like an insult to my mother, and how the story lasted over the years to illustrate how difficult I could be. There is a photograph of me wearing the coat and smashing the eggs that I found on the Easter egg hunt.

Mother told me I could be angry and demanding until I was "taught" to behave differently. Being "taught" means that Mother would have me get a branch off a nearby bush which she then used on my legs. One time I remember, she switched me as punishment for "not letting the cat die" (which was my sisters' way of saying I wouldn't let them have their turns on the swing).

One evening, while mother was sitting in her rocking chair in the soft light, my older sister and I were roller-skating in the house. We had only one pair of skates, so we each had one skate. In my four-year-old heart, I wanted the skate for my right foot, which she had, so I pushed her to get it. With my mother's instant anger, the playful, homey feeling in the room changed immediately. I clearly recall my fear of her anger and being shamed for what I had done.

Still the Wrong Child

In the summer of 1942, during World War II, just before I turned six, we left the nice home my parents built and moved in with my maternal grandmother, who lived a hundred miles away from the paternal family. During the years we lived with my grandmother, there were a few events I remember that gave me a bad feeling. That bad feeling was associated somewhere in my young mind with being ignored, which I later could define as "the wrong child" feeling.

Once year I asked why a favorite aunt (my father's youngest sister) had not given me a birthday present, while she had given presents to my sisters. The next year at my birthday, she gave me a bracelet, and – to everyone's horror – I dropped it on the floor and stomped on it. Of course, I was angry because she had hurt my heart, making me feel she did not love me in the same way she loved my sisters.

Our aunt tried once again at Christmas, giving me little rabbit-looking slippers. I refused to let anyone put them on my feet. The strange rabbit slippers frightened me, but I knew I was refusing her gift for some other reason.

My place in the family was graphically demonstrated to me on another occasion when I was eleven or twelve. We were visiting my paternal grandparents, who had sold the cotton farm and moved to the city. My four aunts, my father's sisters, were also there. In the early evening they took pictures of my sisters, carefully arranging them in good lighting. The pictures were lovely, showing their youthful fourteen- and sixteen-year-old beauty. None were taken of me. I felt they did not take pictures of me because I was not pretty.

Later, my sisters and I were on our sleeping pallets on the floor. The aunts all gathered around my sisters and talked and laughed with them. They sat with their backs to me, so I was not included in the circle. At this point, I could only feel that, besides not being pretty like my sisters, there must be something else I didn't understand. I was left with painful heart feelings, so I remained sad and quiet.

On a trip to Louisiana years later, I visited my last living aunt, who was eighty-seven. As I was getting in my car, ready to drive away, my aunt called out, "We loved you, even though you weren't a boy." I thought I heard correctly. I closed the car door and started back towards her, but she closed her door, and I heard the lock. I called and knocked, but she would not respond. She was not deaf. I felt that she knew I might ask for more information about the family.

I believe no one in the family knew, or even gave it any thought, that as a child, I was harmed by their attitude that I was "the wrong child," and that I would carry that hurt into later years. My identity was distorted further by being viewed and referred to as "the baby" or as "little sister," which left me feeling that my personhood was not recognized.

To this day, I'll ask one of my sisters, "Do you remember what I was like when we were growing up?"

They'll say, "Oh, you were the baby," or, "You were my little sister." I always feel they are saying something they think is sweet and positive. If I question them more, they only repeat the same thought even if rephrased a little differently.

As to how I lived, I appeared to be treated no differently from my sisters. We all enjoyed our friends, did many of the school activities together, and felt we had a secure home that extended into our communities.

A Complicated Mother

Looking back, I can see that my mother was confusing for me. I could count on her motherly care, but at the same time, with each of us she relived different aspects of her childhood traumas that remained in her inner world.

Mother's early traumas affected us, her children. As I understand posttraumatic stress disorder now, whenever she was stressed beyond a certain limit physically or emotionally, she would be triggered into a reaction from her inner world that she did not have the strength to control. She did not intend to be a hurtful, mean, or a traumatizing mother, but she could be and was. She was vulnerable and so were we, her children, because she did not have within her the feeling of having been loved, so it was difficult for her to sustain the love that children need. Despite this, she took care of us in our daily life through her natural instincts in a way that supported a healthy side of our development.

Although she had been traumatized by her parents, she had the intelligence to know that college and a career would be important for her future, and she had the strength of will and determination to manage to complete college on her own. This was around 1922, when college was not that usual for a young woman from her status in life (she was born in 1905).

The fateful event in my mother's life was that, before she was born, her parents' firstborn child died at the age of two or three years old. This child was blond and blue-eyed and was held up as almost an angel. My mother, the next child, arrived with brown curly hair, gray eyes, and dark skin, a complexion like her mother's. As a child, my mother lived with the hurt of unfavorable comparison to the lost angel. In addition, her parents gave her chores like getting up early to start the wood stove to warm the house for them – not something an angel would be asked to do, or even a loved child.

Many times over the years, Mother told us about the time her father tied her to railroad tracks. His primitive brutality was part of his alcoholism. I listened in horror to this story and others, and I felt sad for this little girl, my mother.

Now as a young mother herself, her first living child was blond and blue-eyed. My sister was beautiful, but as she grew up, she was harmed by the anger and judgments Mother constantly directed at her. Mother would be triggered and scream at her for something she had not done. She also had a way of commenting on little things in a way that had the long-term effect of undermining my sister's feelings about herself.

I remember looking at my sister and saying to myself, "Please straighten up," because I saw she was stooping over. As I understood much later, her body posture expressed an inward feeling of being broken. At the same time, Mother gave her the role of the most intelligent child, and she could be motherly and caring towards her as well.

Mother's second daughter was born with brown curly hair and gray-blue eyes, like her own. Her excitement and pleasure in this daughter started at birth and continued all her life. She was a completely different person with this daughter, who was given the role of the one who was cute, fun, and had a fairy-tale quality. Mother showered this daughter with the loving attention that had been denied to her as a child, but might have been bestowed on the lost angel. My mother's inner world colored our daily life.

In the atmosphere created by the different roles each played in our mother's feelings, my two sisters were often embroiled with each other by jealousy, envy, and competition. I was not drawn into their tangle.

However, Mother's inner world affected me in other ways. Family and friends often commented on my resemblance to my mother, to which she was fond of replying, "Oh, yes. She's ugly, just like me."

Each time, I would say, "Please, don't say that," because it was hurtful.

She would say, "Well, it's true," which would increase the hurt for me.

I would look at her with belief but also confusion and think, "But she's pretty."

As a child and adolescent, the impact on my identity was immense.

Later, I realized she identified me with herself as the child who was made to feel ugly and unwanted, but it had the painful lifetime effect on me.

With her husband as well, Mother accepted the role of the ugly, darker servant, one who could be taken for granted and expect neither love nor appreciation. So far as I knew, she contained her rage and resentment. But eventually she took over the family and established her independence from him. In this way she revealed his neediness and incapacity of taking care of the family or himself.

Like my mother, I developed an underground rage because I felt discounted, and I was made to feel ugly, all of which gave me bad feelings about myself. In my quietly defensive, stubborn way, I was determined to make it in my own way.

But as a child, I also developed a strong desire to change myself. I wanted to be someone whom my parents loved and in whom they felt pleasure. Later, I realized that I had developed the fantasy that the only thing that would have pleased my parents and brought me their love was to have been born a boy. Not knowing this was merely a fantasy, I was left in an impossible conundrum; a combination of perfectionism and a sense of failure developed within me.

A Family Myth Exploded

One evening we were talking quietly, when suddenly Phil said, "Wait a minute! This whole story does not make sense, and it does not hold together! I never thought of this."

He went over the whole story and set it straight. My grandfather was not some potentate whose empire relied on his having another male in the line of heritage. As to the family name, my grandfather had two brothers in Louisiana and at least two more in Texas – same family name. The family name was not going to be lost. What a bunch of nonsense!

As to the farm, my grandfather did have a male heir – my father. But my father had no intention of taking over the farm. He didn't want to, and besides, he simply would not have managed. My birth had nothing to do with this.

For that matter, my grandfather had five daughters. Many farmers would have been more than happy to have one or two – or five – daughters take over their farm. Women running a farm was not an issue. And one might marry a farmer.

Neither I nor Phil had ever thought to question another side of my familiar story that had to do with my father.

His five sisters put him on a pedestal and kept him there all his life. "He was wonderful, could do no wrong, so funny, a

wonderful father and provider – a very special man." This was
the family myth, and it was utter nonsense.

No matter what they saw, his family was determined to
hold on to their illusion. They were not able to acknowledge
the reality of who he was. He was an undeveloped person who
had limited capacity for functioning in the world.

Maybe his sisters felt that there should be some explana-
tion for his ineptness – beyond the obvious reality. The family
story about his having three daughters and no sons – leaving
me as the wrong child – was a distraction and a cover. It allowed
them to maintain my father in everyone's eyes as the special
son and brother of the family. It protected the family myth.
The story about the great disappointment of my birth served
as a cover story.

CHAPTER 4

Growing Up in Small Towns in the South

Birth Town and Land

From my birth to a few years after I completed college, my family lived in four small towns. Three of the four towns were within twenty miles of each other. My parents then moved one last time to a new home they built in the same area. The town where I was born and where we lived for five years was only a hundred miles from the others. It was settled around 1830 on the Macon Bayou. Many of the small towns were settled on bayous for transportation of goods. A bayou, unlike a swamp, has clear water and a slow-flowing current like a river, and in the South, the bald cypress trees draped in Spanish moss grow all through them, creating a uniquely enchanting vista. To reach my grandparents' front yard from our property, we had to cross the bayou on a small bridge.

My paternal grandmother's family was one of the early families that settled here. She was born in 1882, and I have memories of her telling stories she heard from her parents of how the Northern Army under Sherman marched through the South during the Civil War, laying waste to all they came across. I do not remember details from her stories, only lingering feelings of fear and anger.

Grandfather's farm was by most standards large, and they had a large farmhouse, but it was not one of the great Southern plantations. The endless fields of cotton were a prominent feature of the landscape. This farm and all the areas where I grew up left lasting impressions of natural beauty and of a slow, soft pace of my life as a child.

When I was maybe in the sixth grade, I made a memory book of the history of Louisiana. I did not know there was another deep part of the soul of the state – the history of slavery, secession, horrors of lynching, the hate and humiliation of segregation, distrust of Yankees, and holding the honor of the Confederate flag as commemorating the bravery of the rebels. I did not learn the serious history of slavery and the connection to the Confederate symbols. A part of the culture was the haunting unresolved loss of the Civil War. Without the awareness of this painful history, I lived freely and usually in safety as a white child of the American South.

Changing Towns

Soon after America entered World War II, we moved to the small farm recently purchased by my mother's mother. It was in a rural community of small farms, and it had a Baptist church and a two-room schoolhouse. I began school here, and Mother returned to teaching that year in the same school. We lived with my maternal grandmother for three years.

When the war ended in 1945, we moved ten miles to a rural town where we lived until just before my fourteenth birthday.

Then we moved again, this time to the larger college town where I finished high school. I went to a Louisiana state college, where I earned my degree in nursing.

These moves during my childhood were not disturbing or disruptive for me. Each place was not that far from all the others, so we maintained our contacts with extended family and friends. Besides, culturally, they were all more or less identical, and we were accepted and felt at home in each community.

Segregation was a way of life in the South from the time I was born in 1936 to the year I graduated from college in 1958. In the small towns in which I grew up, African Americans had their own part of town and their own schools and churches. Beneath the friendly, peaceful surface, there were (and still are) deeper and darker layers. Many writers have probed these layers, none more profoundly and movingly than Lillian Smith in *Killers of the Dream* ([1949] 1961).

The towns of the South were also defined by virtually universal Christianity. Church life had a prominent place in the lives of most families and wherever we were, my family was actively engaged with a Southern Baptist church.

We were part of the white middle class that was developing after the war. The small towns we lived in were still informal and communal, providing relationships that sometimes eased the difficulties of sustaining our modest way of life. Banks were neighborly and less formal. Mother regularly went to our local bank for small loans, slowly paying them back as she could. The give-and-take of a neighborly network allowed flexibility in managing family expenses.

I remember seeing Mother at the kitchen table, where I sometimes joined her, as she paid the bills and carefully made a hopeful budget for the next month. She worried about meeting expenses, but she wanted to allow for movies and other social activities. This kind of careful awareness about expenses has stayed with me to this day.

Two or three more well-established families in town often lent a hand to neighbors. When my sisters and I were teenagers one family helped us. They allowed Mother to keep a running tab at their grocery store, and the husband helped my father find jobs.

The wife of this couple was a younger woman who was an elementary school teacher like my mother, and almost every day they shared their stories and problems. I would say, "Here comes Abby," because it seemed she could hardly wait for Mother to come home so she could visit. They seemed to treasure the time together.

This young couple enjoyed introducing me and my two sisters to special activities. The wife invited many of my class-mates to a luncheon for me when I graduated from high school. I helped their family by babysitting for their youngest son. I took him to his first days of school. On the first day, he was frightened and trembling, so I held him close until we could leave for the day. Our families shared and supported each other in these many ways.

Four Strands

I discern four interwoven strands in my development during those years in the South. I have described the first strand, which relates to my birth as a female and as "the wrong child." Parents and extended family wove me into their story, which entered my unspoken beliefs about myself and affected my identity for the rest of my life.

Another strand of my development – a healthy one – is based in my connection with nature. The farms of my first two homes and our later rural home were surrounded by meadows and woods, with streams nearby. I loved being alone, out of doors in nature, playing and exploring. I always had a pet dog as well as other animal pets like a rooster, rabbits, and a pig. My connection with nature nurtured, held, and grounded me.

My relationship with my mother is the basis for a third strand of my development. She functioned productively in the world. In addition to her teaching, she was often involved with school activities and the 4-H Club, and she had friends.

By the time I was thirteen or fourteen, she had primary responsibility for the family economy. She made sure her three daughters went to college. She had this inner strength and health. My identification with her provided me with the values, habits, and tools that allowed me to hold responsible jobs and support myself, often in the face of serious limitations.

My relationship with my father is the basis for the fourth strand of my development. He was an undeveloped person and was disturbed in ways that became worse as he got older. I did not have a father who supported my development or who was a man who modeled a healthy, productive, and loving way of life.

In my adult years, despite obstacles in my development, I had my strengths and resources. I felt good about working in a career and taking care of myself. In addition, I had the curiosity and independence that led to my decision to leave the South and led me to continuously develop in my work and my personal life.

I left the South for the last time in 1967. I chose to move to the northeast, an entirely different culture. The Boston/Cambridge area of Massachusetts became my home for the next forty-seven years.

CHAPTER 5

The War Years

Grandmother's Farm

The war years, 1942–1946, stand out as a distinct period in my childhood, and I enjoy looking back at the child I was then. As a six-year-old, moving to live with my maternal grandmother meant fresh explorations in fields, creeks, and woods. The house was new, large, and to my eyes, filled with wonderful conveniences. There was plenty of hot running water in the house, a kitchen with a new gas stove and a refrigerator. All of this must have been a treat for my mother.

My grandmother purchased this small farm, with its well-built house, for her youngest son who, along with his two brothers, were in military service in Europe during World War II. She needed my parents to help her until her son returned from the war.

Compared with my grandfather's cotton farm, this was a small, family farm. But it had a lot of exciting, different features that impressed me. The extensive surrounding woods with all kinds of different trees and a creek were different after the bayou with its moss-draped cypress trees. In addition to all this, besides the main house, I was enchanted by three other small houses on the property. The smallest was perfect for us to use as a playhouse. Another one near the back steps was used for clothes washing, tool storage, and other things. Finally, there was a larger house used by my mother's injured brother when he came back from the war.

There still other features of this property that I found unusual and interesting. There was a huge water tank as tall as the house for catching rainwater to water the garden, and there was a garage with three large sections for cars and storage. Away from the house there was a large vegetable garden and sheds for animals.

The whole property had been beautifully and functionally developed. The main house was made from the best materials, and large trees were allowed to remain in the yard near the house.

I loved the new activities in my life, and now I was old enough to feel my experiences as my own. I had woods to explore with my dog, and a small creek with cool water to wade in that felt wonderful on my feet in the summer. In the fall, joining in with everybody to rake the beautiful leaves was a step, if only a small one, from being *the baby* to being more like my sisters.

The new activity that meant the most to me was starting school, which I had been looking forward to. And not only that, but also my mother returned to teaching, which she loved. In the mornings during good weather, going to school was an adventure, because Mother, myself, and my two sisters all walked along a dirt road to the two-room school, about a mile away. We were joined on the way by a few other children. Now I belonged to this little group and the larger group – the longed-for school world. I had my own desk and books! We had recess for play! We all ate lunch together! And there were all these children for me to be with! School was perfect!

My Family's Life on Grandmother's Farm

At thirty-eight, my mother's life shifted dramatically when we moved in with her mother, and for a while I had the feeling that she was happy. Even with hard work, life was easier for her. She was away from the complications of living with her in-laws. She enjoyed the conveniences of a new house, and my sisters and I were old enough to help more. Living with or near my father's family for ten years, her life had hardly been her own. She had four pregnancies during these years, and with her last one (me), her depression started.

She had been breaking down emotionally and physically and needed a change. Now she was able to return to teaching, earn her own income, and her children were all in school. She was with her mother, and they worked together gardening, caring for the house, cooking, and taking care of us. They had a natural way of working cooperatively together that supported my mother emotionally and physically. Her mother could be dominating but my mother knew how to work hard; teaching school allowed them to have separate time, and she knew that we wouldn't be living there after the war ended..

With Father's job and Mother working too, my family's financial situation was much improved, giving Mother a feeling of security and strength. For Father, now aged forty-two, my impression is that the time living on Grandmother's farm was a good period in his life. We lived closer to his work, and it was the best job he would have in his life. At this time, being in the army reserves and wearing his uniform were sources of pride.

We lived closer to what I called a city. We had new experiences of shopping, and there were many new sights that impressed me, like a large hotel with grand steps up to the entrance, a large hall and a grand stairway, and a cafe (for hot chocolate). It was here that I saw the glue on Santa's beard – an observation that revealed the truth about this myth.

Excitement, Sex, Hell

During our second year on the farm, my sisters started in the "big school." Now they got to ride a school bus, and I was left out of what I imagined as the best part of being in school. I did ride with them one day to visit their school. In the afternoon I was so excited on the way home that I could not stay in my seat. I was calling – probably yelling – goodbye to all the children I had fallen in love with during the day. The bus driver walked back down the aisle from his seat looking frightening and angry and told me to sit down and be quiet.

I remember freezing in place and being terrified; my body drooped with guilt about my loud, joyful expressions. I was probably eight years old, and I knew the feelings of guilt and humiliation. My intense excitement had gotten me in trouble in earlier years, so I was already in the process of learning that excitement is wrong, not how it could be a healthy joyful expression. Southern culture looked on girls' excitement with caution and disdain. If a girl's excitement was not brought under control, it meant that later her sexual excitement would not be under control, and that meant trouble.

The whole weight of the Southern Baptist church supported this attitude. If something "bad" happened, it would be the girl's fault. I did not consciously grasp what I was being taught, but I developed a fear of my excitement before I was aware of what the word "sex" meant. Besides that, I could hear in the teaching that there was a place called "Hell" – a horrible, frightening place. In my mind, as a little girl, excitement, sex, and Hell all intermingled into a fearful, confused chaos that seared into my being.

Darkness

In my mind there has always been a dark shadow over this period in my life. For a long time, I wondered about the source of that awareness. There were some external factors. These were war years, 1942 to 1945. I did not understand what war was, but it felt like something frightening and bad. Everyone listened to the radio war news. Food was rationed, but we had plenty of our own from our garden and animals.

One day we all went to the movies and during the intermission war news films were shown. They were frightening and loud. I stood up on my seat, and said, "I don't like this kind of church. Take me home."

One of Mother's brothers, who had been in the navy, returned home with a metal plate in his skull. He lived in a small house on the farm and medicated himself with alcohol. Sometimes we heard him screaming in pain, which was frightening for me.

I heard about people roaming around the countryside during those years, adding another fear to my imagination. The war, the injured, and the unsettled feeling in society – all cast frightening shadows over these times in my feelings. But I was vulnerable to these fears because of another fear closer to me.

A Room Not of My Own

For the three years living with Grandmother, between the ages of six and nine, my parents had me sleeping in their bedroom. My small bed was only a few feet away from the foot of their bed. This is the source of the dark aura that hangs over this period for me.

This arrangement exposed me, for all the nights of those years, to my parents' sexual life and to whatever else was in their intimate night life. This arrangement constituted a violation of my sexual development. It could be called sexual abuse, and it left a scar.

The arrangement was entirely unnecessary, and it was totally inappropriate. There was plenty of space for me in my sisters' room, or I could have used the small cot under the dining room windows where I took afternoon naps.

While I have many varied memories from that period, I have no memories of anything seen, heard, or felt in that bedroom in all those nights. But, on the other hand, I have had a multiplicity of disquieting bodily experiences expressive of my sexual disturbance and difficulties, which could well have originated in what I felt during those nights.

Many years later I asked my mother why they put me, as a child, in their bedroom. She looked blank and did not offer an answer. I did not have the emotional strength or the developed understanding that would have allowed me to pursue my question.

CHAPTER 6

My Life Opens

Mythology's identification of woman with
nature is correct.

– Camille Paglia, *Sexual Personae* (1990)

A Home of Our Own

World War II ended. My mother's youngest brother returned and, although seriously traumatized, took over the running of the farm. Her oldest brother with the terrible injury did not live long after his return, and the middle brother settled down with his wife in a nearby town. The man whose job my father had taken over also returned, so my father had to relinquish the job he had found satisfying.

When the war ended, the two-room school where Mother had been teaching for three years was closed. Now there was federal money to buy school buses, so all the children could be transferred to the large school in a nearby small town. Mother was offered a job teaching fourth grade in that school. As it

happened, I was entering fourth grade, so I was in her class –
there was a total of fifty children in this class that she took on.

We moved once again. Even though this was the second
move in just a few years, it was not disruptive to me or the family.
The town was within ten miles of my grandmother's farm,
and even the cotton farm was not that far away. My parents
purchased a recently built home that sat on ten acres with some
open areas and a small area of woods. There was a creek that ran
along one edge of our property, and I took ownership of it. Best
of all for me, my freedom included sharing a bedroom with my
sisters and no longer having to sleep in my parents' bedroom.

Now my mother had a home of her own, my parents were
both working, and they felt financially secure. We were happy to
experience our mother's excitement about being able to furnish
our home. She bought twin size-beds for me and my sisters, a
new dresser with special drawers for our ribbons, a new long
mirror, and we all went out to buy a new piano – all the things
that I felt were just right for a home with teenage girls.

The years we lived in this small rural town, even with the
difficulties I will describe, were the happiest years for us as a
family. These years were a vital period in my development. I
quickly grew familiar with the children and teachers at school
and church, and with special areas of the town. I felt that I had
my own community, that I belonged in it, and that I was free.
I began to flourish. I believe each member of our family had a
similar experience in finding support in our new small town.

Mother finally managed to get away from her in-laws as
well as her own mother. For that matter, this was the first time
in his life my father had not lived under the auspices of his
father or his wife's mother. It was a new start for both of them.

Homesteading, 1946

Mother's hard work was continuous, with large classes, house-keeping, and cooking. She needed our help and asked us to do what we could, but she also wanted us to have freedom to play and have our life as children. She knew what it was like to lose childhood to work.

My father found a part-time job with the County Agriculture Department. He maintained and fixed up our home. He never attempted to farm on his father's land, but at our place he turned into a farmer just for our family. He established a large vegetable garden, he built coops for chickens and hutches for our pet rabbits, fenced in a yard for our pet pig, and added a new shed for our milk cows.

My father's one passion was his honeybees. He was known for his skills as a beekeeper, and he was called on to capture escaped bee swarms. He did not turn his skills into a source of income, but he enjoyed bringing in the honey for family and friends to enjoy.

There were two grocery stores, but in the 1940s in these small towns they did not provide fresh meat and vegetables. For our meat, my parents made arrangements with whoever might be butchering an animal, and since we did not have small home freezers then, they rented space in large freezer lockers at the school. We kept chickens for eating and fresh eggs.

For the rest of our food, we depended on what we produced ourselves, so it was hard work for both parents. There were mature fig, pecan, and plum trees on our property, and even a small grove of mulberry trees. Mother made jellies and jams from our fruit, she canned vegetables from our garden, and the potatoes were stored under the hay barn. This preserved food took us through the winter. I loved the cold nights when she made creamed tomato soup and we were all together eating around the fireplace.

Our homesteading was a necessity for our family's well-being. It required careful planning throughout the year. Most families we knew sustained themselves in this way.

Our father arranged special play areas for us. He tamped down the clay and put up a basketball hoop. We had three swings now and he built stilts for us, great for learning balance and building strength. My oldest sister wrote plays, and she put them on with our friends in the small hay barn near the house. We would often have our friends in on Sunday afternoons and make candy or ice cream.

Our mother planted flowers, which she loved. I especially remember the tea roses she used to make corsages on special occasions such as piano recitals. I enjoyed every area of the property. In the woods I could sit in my "chinquapin tree," be quiet, and listen to the sounds of the world around me – again, there was the feeling of freedom.

My Life

When we moved, I entered my mother's fourth-grade class. In comparison with my previous two-room school, this one was large. It was a short walk from home to the school, and teachers and friends joined us along the way. My mother had friends here, so in the beginning, we were happy. We felt welcomed and accepted into our small town.

I thoroughly enjoyed going to school. Being in my mother's class of fourth graders had its problems, but I remember only a few difficulties. This same year, I discovered boys were cute and interesting, which made it an important year for my sexual development. At recess, most often, I would join in a tag game with the boy I chose for that day or week. One boy had chosen me and brought me a gift every morning. It could be a small flower, one stick of gum, sometimes bubblegum, which was popular, and other items he thought I might like. I liked him too, and his childhood love warmed my developing sense of myself as a little girl. My mother did not at any time interfere with my newfound excitement with boys.

I enjoyed my girlfriends, and I had one best friend, who lived with her grandparents on a sugar cane farm not far from the school. I had the freedom to visit her often and loved to visit when they were making the sugar cane syrup. I watched the horses go around and around grinding the juice from the cane. Nearby, huge vats for evaporating the juice sat over dramatic wood fires.

These people were special to me, a part of my own community. Their way of life would soon change forever. I cherish having had the chance to be with them and feel a part of it.

A painful, sad memory, involving my father and my best friend is associated with the memories of the sugar cane farm. To make a little extra money, her grandparents let her sell syrup to friends and neighbors. One day when she came to our house with her jars of syrup, my father started teasing her in a senseless, demeaning way. He said she was "peddling," which to me and to her meant something bad, although we did not know what it was. I remember how her face lost the open look of my friend, and she seemed to shrink away from me. I became upset and pained to see him hurt her. And then he laughed at both of us and went on with something else. We were left with our unresolved feelings.

His family and others viewed this kind of teasing as his way of communicating and treated it as if it were fun. I knew from early that it was not fun. It was wounding. I was frequently hurt by experiencing him teasing my mother, her friends, and my friends, and I was wounded when he directed it at me.

Of course, I was not capable of expressing this awareness to anyone at the time.

Summers and Camp

My sixth-grade teacher was our neighbor. When in her class I was often excited and in good spirits, and I liked to talk with my friends in the back of the room. She liked to tell the story about an attempt she made to stop me chatting so much in class. She asked me to move more to the front of the room. But I said, "Oh no, I can hear much better back here." She said she could not stop quietly laughing to herself, and at that point, she did not push for me to do as she asked. I felt accepted and liked by all my elementary school teachers. My seventh-grade teacher was important because she understood my need to be myself and not try to measure up to my sisters. Her sensitivity was a critical support for me as a thirteen-year-old.

I went to Sunday school every week, and in the summer, there was a week of Bible camp. To be able to attend, we had to memorize Bible verses and have an adult of the church listen and give us a pass. This study interfered with my free time, and I had great difficulty focusing and memorizing. The verses from the Bible did not make sense to me; they seemed to be in a totally different language. Our neighbor, my sixth-grade teacher, helped as much as she could by teaching me how to memorize the verses anyway. I remember the feeling of acceptance as I sat with her on her porch steps.

My sisters and I carefully prepared our camp clothes. I enjoyed this ritual, and I was excited about taking the train. I vividly remember the three of us with our suitcases waiting and then boarding the train with help from our mother. The pleasure of this camp was mixed. I enjoyed the activities, but the daily church services were difficult.

Our one week of 4-H camp was pure enjoyment for me. I was engaged and happy. My best friend as well as my sisters were with me, and Mother was a counselor. Our father would come out in the evenings and have dinner with the campers, making it a family experience.

During the days we formed small groups, decided on a name for ourselves, planned projects, and learned to collaborate. In the evening, the older members enjoyed their own social life, and we younger members played numerous running games that we made up and chased armadillos when they appeared.

I loved all the ongoing physical activity, but swimming was my favorite. The first time I was allowed to go swimming, it was a total, unbelievable, joyful experience. I can still recall the wonder of the cool water on my body and the feeling of joy.

Once I found myself in a situation where I might have drowned, but my best friend and swimming partner called for help, so I was kept out of danger. When our father came out to the camp that evening, I heard him talking with mother. He was saying I should not be allowed to go swimming, and mother insisted that it was more important for me to continue and learn how to swim. Her view was the final decision.

Growing up I always had dogs to play with, but I also had other pets. One of the most outstanding was a beautiful red rooster. He won first place at the state fair. A picture of my pet rooster and I made the front page of the local newspaper. I still have this picture. It shows my rooster standing on a low, open shelf in front of me, looking proud and regal. I am totally focused as I reach out to him, not touching him, but holding a space around him with a feeling of tenderness expressed by my hands and eyes.

My summers during these years brought me a child's experience of timelessness. They seemed endless. The weather was soft, warm, and sunny, or sometimes with dramatic, exciting thunderstorms. I was allowed a lot of freedom, so I could immerse myself in the sensuousness of my moment-to-moment activities.

My Life Disturbed

By the third year, my sisters and I sensed that all was not going well with our parents. Mother would sometimes lock herself in the guest room. There was a gun in that room. We were frightened, not knowing what she might do. Would she shoot herself? We did not know any particulars but saw that our mother was disturbed and unhappy. Even so, it seems revealing that our thoughts were that alarming.

Then I witnessed something that upset me. Mother needed to have surgery. For whatever reason, my father did not drive her to the hospital. My heart broke watching her walk down the street carrying her small suitcase to get the bus or train. How could this be?

I often could not comprehend my father's behavior in relation to my mother. I saw her look of pain many times. I felt he was cruel to her, but it was hard for me to believe that about my father. However, just as I was entering puberty, he did something that injured me terribly, and this time, I had no question as to his cruelty. I was thirteen. It was our final year of living in my favorite town. Some details are not clear in my memory, but I am clear about the core of the event that affected me.

One sunny, warm evening I went to an ice cream party sponsored by the church for the children. I wore a beautiful dress with a wide sash, and I was extremely excited. One of the boys, who was a year older, asked if he could drive me home in his family's jeep. His invitation excited me further. This was almost like a real date! My first!

When I came into the house, my father was in a rage. First, he ridiculed the boy and the boy's family in an appalling, demeaning way. Next, he turned his rage on me. It made no sense to me, and I do not remember his words. I could only feel that his rage was because of my excitement about being with a boy.

His attack was sudden and without warning and upset me horribly for several days. Mother allowed me to stay home from school. But she did not help me understand what had happened, to alleviate the effects of my father's rage. The whole experience was a shock that left permanent damage to my social and sexual development.

Daily freedom to explore the natural world was a large part of my healthy sexual development along with beginning the perfect world of school. However, sleeping in my parents' bedroom for three years left the dark shadow of abuse. When we moved and I was out of their bedroom, I regained my natural movement for continuing my sexual development. At age thirteen after my father's horrible, raging attack, I was again changed. My excitement was no longer as spontaneous, and I started taking special care to not draw attention to myself. There were no more dates.

Other later experiences registered in my being as well. One high school teacher in this town was cruel. She would compare me unfavorably to my older sister with comments about my looks and the way I dressed. Another time she remarked that I walked "like I had one leg shorter than the other," since my pelvis would swing when I walked. I had already become extremely sensitive to any remark about being sexual, so her words frightened me and made me self-conscious about my looks and my walk.

Until then, my walk had remained free. After my father's attack, I had been resilient enough to be able to get back to enjoying being a girl at least to this extent. However, at this point, my resilience was fragile. These attacks from the teacher started the inhibition of that free movement. My pelvis tightened, and I began developing what I call the typical, Southern "good girl" walk. The lifetime of all I took in on some level from birth around my identity as a girl now became attached to insecurity of how to dress and walk.

After four years, we left our home in this small town. I had finished seventh grade. The day we moved, there was a light rain. It was a sad day for me. While my parents were packing, I took an umbrella and walked alone all around our property. I loved the little house we lived in, the neighborhood, my pets, my creek, my bicycle-riding areas, my school being so close, my best friend nearby, and feeling accepted by my teachers in those early years. I was saying my goodbye.

The College Town

We moved about twenty miles to the town where my oldest sister was in college, and where Mother had lived as a child. She said we needed to move so my sister could live at home, and we could afford her college expenses. She continued teaching at the same school, and I continued school there for three more years, driving the twenty miles with her, until I completed the tenth grade (with the teacher who had previously made the comment about my "short-leg walk").

The summer after I finished tenth grade, a new, modern high school had just been completed only a meadow away from our now home. I transferred, knowing I would have better preparation for college. I had already made friends with two girls who lived only two blocks away, so we could all walk to school together.

I was ready to leave the school I had been going to since the fourth grade and I started the new school feeling excited.

Unfortunately, the following months did not fulfill the promise of that good start. The earlier attacks on my budding sexuality proved to be a prelude to more deeply traumatic experiences in these last two years of high school, affecting me far into my life.

PART III

Phil

We do not exist for the sake of something else.
We exist for the sake of ourselves.

– Shunryu Suzuki, *Zen Mind, Beginner's Mind* (1970)

CHAPTER 7

The History of Marriages

Parents' Marriage

As a boy, my parents' marriage was a given, the bedrock of my stable world. I never thought of them as "being married" or "having a relationship." They were together, my mom and dad. At the same time, I got the impression that they were not happy together. When I was a little older, I articulated my impression by thinking, "There is something going on under the surface," a thought I shared with no one. From early on, my credo was, "When I grow up, I will do something I like." This applied to work and to my fantasies about who I would marry and what it would be like for me to have a family.

Even before adolescence, judgments were evolving in my mind. They grew out of what I felt and experienced being around my parents and observing them. I could also compare my parents with the parents of other families we knew. My judgments and criticisms evolved slowly over the years, but still remained at the edges of my consciousness, and they never reached the level of overt, articulated criticism. Emotionally, for me, they were who they were, and I didn't expect them to be different.

My observations of them fueled my imagination as to how I wanted my life to be when I grew up. I knew I wanted my life as an adult to be different. I didn't have the language to describe what I was responding to in my parents, but the body feelings were clear to me. Now I can articulate what I missed in my parents' relationship and in our life together. It all had to do with warmth, warm contact among the family members, enjoyment of each other, and liveliness and enjoyment of life. On the rare occasions when I was with a warm, responsive adult who was ready to enjoy me, I could feel it in my body. I could feel excitement when it was there, curiosity, and a sense of adventure. These are all the things I wanted, and I felt my parents, because of who they were, did not join in these aspects of life.

At the same time, I admired my father. From my perspective as a child, it took a strong, self-sacrificing man like my father to meet the duties and carry the burden of work and family. And he was a strong man. He was strong physically, and he had a good character. He took care of us, worked hard, and people respected him. At times he conveyed quiet ease and contentment. He loved to putter with small projects in his basement shop, and in this mode, we built a telegraph system around the basement.

As a boy and even much later, I could not tell if his work gave him satisfaction. I never heard or saw him express gratification or enjoyment about his job, or, for that matter, about his family. His unbroken heaviness bothered me. I worried about him and felt guilty. I questioned, "Was he doing all this for me?"

Just as troubling, as a boy I interpreted his heaviness as reflecting what it was like for him to be with my mother. As I admired my father, so I felt critical of my mother. I saw her as a burden for my father. She often seemed nervous and unstable. While Dad seemed burdened, but stalwart, she frequently let it be known that her share of family responsibilities was too much for her. Her stress showed in irritability, frequent fatigue, headaches, and gastrointestinal problems. She seemed mostly preoccupied with how to manage herself, her fragile digestive system, and her nerves.

I saw her tension, anxiety, and chronic symptoms as a constant drag on the mood of the family. I didn't see her enjoying herself or having fun. She didn't seem to enjoy me or feel warmly towards me; instead, she worried about me. She didn't talk to me or take an interest in what I was interested in or what I did.

The critical feelings I built up towards my mother kept me from appreciating her contributions to our comfort and well-being. Even with her chronic malaise, she was constant and reliable in the management of the home. She always carefully prepared – sometimes with hired help – an evening meal for her husband and children. But at the supper table, with the slightest hint of conflict or raised voices, Mother would suddenly gasp in pain, grasping her breast or her head. Her reactions were dramatic, and they frightened and worried me. My father, too, reacted with fear and apprehension. I didn't know if she was dying, and maybe I caused it. Dad's look was scary, but I was also repulsed by my mother's gestures, which gave me added reason for guilt.

At other times, she took some small tension as an indication we did not appreciate her. "I washed every piece of that lettuce by hand," she said. And on another occasion, the poignant complaint, "I'm blamed for everything." Her tension made me tense and kept me quiet. At many of these mealtimes,

I had no appetite. Unable to eat, I pushed the food around on my plate and filled my mouth with tasteless stuff I could not swallow.

Traditional Folks

Born in 1900, Mother took on the traditional woman's role that was expected of women at that time: looking after her husband, house, and children. Before meeting my father, she attended secretarial school and worked in that capacity for a few years (she had beautiful handwriting).

Mother diligently provided Dad with the home base that kept him steady and allowed him to manage the stress of his job and shouldering the responsibilities of wife, house, and kids. As years passed, she was more prone to somatic-emotional complaints and easily upset. Being wife and mother, in my father's house, wore her down. What was most distressing to see was her energy pulling in and quieting down more and more. She rested more and communicated less, until in her last decade she reached an equilibrium with little movement, where she still functioned just enough to not be completely bedridden.

My dad was born in 1897, so of course his attitudes were patriarchal. Instinctively I felt he held negative attitudes toward my mother, although knowing what his attitudes were bordered on the impossible because of his lack of expressiveness and verbal communication. However, I am quite sure that my "treatment" of women reflected my father's treatment of my mother. As times changed, my patriarchal attitudes became obvious to me: my tendency to assume I was the foundation of the couple, the strong one, a bit superior, a bit domineering; and I could be impatient, irritable, and dismissive. As I painfully worked to change, I often felt my father's influence.

They did not quarrel, and they never overtly criticized

each other. Dad was not overtly expressive of affection or sexuality, but as far as I know, that was a regular part of their life together. In the safety and constancy of their connection, my parents were faithful, caring companions to the end of their days. They shared the rhythms and cycles of their whole adult lives, marrying, having children, my father having his career, grandchildren arriving, and having two quiet decades in retirement. They lived carefully, peacefully, and comfortably. Except for the occasion when they were attacked by my brother and his wife, they kept distress at bay. They each found times of quiet contentment, often separately and alone, but sometimes together, and sometimes, as during the war, the three of us together.

Their connection, with its quiet stability, was a source of security for me. Nevertheless, my impression of their life together never evolved into a vision that I wanted to emulate.

With me they were blandly laissez-faire. I went my own way, on my own, even in grade school. I had almost no communication with them, separately or together. In relation to them, my experience and my emotional life remained unnamed and unspoken, becoming a part of my inner world. Being a part of my inner world meant they were not experienced in the context of a relationship with another person, making them readily available for fueling shame and disturbance, and – for that matter – building grounds for my negative impression of my parents' life together.

Sibs

My brother and sister chose their partners and married when I was fifteen and sixteen. Their marriages distressed me, at times almost to the point of horror. On the infrequent occasions when I was with either of them, I was pained to see the effects of the stress they lived under. My siblings' relationships, from my perspective, were filled with conflict, unhappiness, and even hate. I thought they each paid a heavy price in terms of health and personal well-being.

"Coming of Age"

My personal history of my family's marriages did not offer a useful guide for me, except in a negative way. I was ill prepared to enter the exploratory phase of adolescent dating.

My wants and desires remained in the realm of unformed fantasy, and the girl remained out of reach. I was morose, withdrawn, introverted, and inept socially. I was a top student, did many activities, was a good citizen of the school community. As to communicating with girls, I was not in the game and even mute.

I lived through many school days in a haze through which I saw little more than images of girls who were the objects of my desires. I managed to keep my head enough above water so as not to drown, and I retained enough self preservation instinct to reserve a portion of my resources for what I needed to do.

In my sophomore year in high school, Carol apparently took a shine to me. She had a soft swarthiness, a full inviting mouth, and lovely full breasts that unabashedly announced themselves to my longing eyes courtesy of the tight, short-sleeved sweaters she wore daily (Sandy wore sweaters like that too) Oh, I wanted to kiss her so badly! Never happened.

For weeks I watched for Carol in the hallways, eyeing her every time she passed by. Carol did the same until her expression took on the question, "Well?"

It took some weeks, but I finally got enough control over my dread to invite her to the New Year's Eve party I begged my parents to arrange. My father drove me to pick her up and stayed up to take her home. Afterwards, I lay awake the rest of the night, hyper-stimulated and overwrought. We went to the movies once or twice and sat as close together as the seats allowed, but there were none of the longed-for kisses.

The haze thickened in my junior and senior year when a different girl became the object of my longings. I could not get over how anyone could be so utterly adorable. All day I moved through a fog, soggy with an achy, longing preoccupation, images of her floating in my mind. My experience had an unconnected, surreal quality with no way of moving from fantasy world to the real one. After an eon of agonies, I managed to call and ask her to a dance, but by the time of our date, she was not interested. Soon she was another boy's girlfriend.

Besides my fantasy girls, there were attractive, real girls who might have been interested in me. But I did not notice, or what I did notice did not register. My sexual development was going full blast, but my desire had been captured by hidden fantasy and wound up into inner fixations. I did not consciously connect the pleasurable sensations of masturbation with the stimulation of the pretty faces, delicious breasts, lips, and figures of the adorable girls I gawked at day in and day out. My coming of age was delayed, I would say, until my mid-twenties, when I lived in New York City like a beatnik.

CHAPTER 8

Sticky Things

A Little Boy and His Mother

This scene is one of my earliest memories.

It is a warm spring day. My mother is sitting in the passenger seat of a car with the door open. She is sunning herself, as she likes to do. The car is parked by a wide strip of lush green grass filled with sparkling golden dandelions. I am exploring and admiring the dandelions.

I might have been three years old.

As my memory has it, we are in Washington, DC. My father is on vacation, and he and Mother have taken us kids on a trip. My older siblings are visiting the Smithsonian Institute with our father. They decided I am too young for this educational experience, so I am left with my mother.

The dandelions excite me. I feel the beauty of their golden glowing crowns made up of hundreds of sharp little petals. I carefully gather a bouquet, and offer them to my mother. She says, "I don't want those," with an edge of irritation in her voice.

It is unlikely that this memory exactly replicates my original experience. But, for as long as I have been aware of having memories, this was the form it took.

An oddly similar experience occurred many years later. On her birthday one year, when I was in my twenties, I gave my mother a beautiful book on wildflowers. I was excited to give it to her, believing she would enjoy it, because she loved flowers. When she received it, to my disappointment, she had no reaction whatsoever.

Love's Sad Fate

My path to developing the capacity for love led through the unmapped terrain of hate. I came to think that hate must be what happens when love is disappointed or turned against.

When I offered the bouquet of dandelions to my mother, and she rejected it, my love didn't immediately become hate. I don't remember my reaction, but I can easily imagine it.

I see a little boy turning away from his mother. He is looking at the bouquet of dandelions with a confused expression, seeing it in a new light. He feels the sticky, milky sap of the stems. The aroma is unpleasant.

Before his mother's rejection, the flowers glistened in the sun, each one made up of thousands of perfect little jewel-like blades of gold. Now, looking askance at the flowers, he sees a sickly yellow.

He pushes his small hand out away from his body, the hand opens, fingers stiffly extended, mimicking his mother's tone of disgust, letting the dandelions fall limply to the ground making a pile of waste. His movement expresses his feeling that the offer of the bouquet and his love, were wrong, and he is distancing himself from the bad hand, arm, and love feeling, as if he were now two boys, one feeling something akin to disgust for the other.

Now, as I imagine what I might have felt then, feelings surface. I have a sinking, shrinking feeling that begins in the pit of my stomach. More disturbing, I have a sense of a strange kind of chilling aura surrounding me like a shattering, invisible ice-like sheath, and then a kind of blanking out, a helpless absence.

Me, as a self, the little boy I was then, disappeared. His enjoyment of the sun, flowers, and beauty, and the warm feeling for his mother are gone. I was drawn or fell into a sinking feeling and blankness, surrounded by an icy sheath, and I was left there by myself. No one came to find me, so I followed myself into the aloneness and became it.

My life went on. But I was a different boy. My body contracted, my energy withdrew, and I pulled in. I lost the self who moved and loved freely. I was affected through the whole of my body. Out of this contracted body, a sulfurous mix of fear and distrust produced distorted perceptions, the conviction that I will be disappointed and hurt, and an automatic certainty that she dislikes me and hates my sexuality. These are the masks of hate.

Feelings for my mother closed off. Sadly, with Vellie when I felt hurt or disappointed, I would "drop her." I acted as if she hardly existed – a terrible experience for her. Within myself, I felt abandoned, left in my aloneness, reliving some version of what I experienced with my mother.

Many years after I left my childhood home and parents, the determination came to my mind that I had to learn to love. I could feel closeness, warmth, and the pleasure of lovemaking, and I knew that was the most important thing to me. But I did not know love – not when I felt it, not when the woman felt it for me, and not what it had to do with between me and her.

Love and Hate

I cannot say if this memory represents the incident that is the cause of my problematic development over the following years. I can say, without hesitation, that it is a clear model or pattern for my development in relation to women. Contraction (deep body tensions) and self-distancing shaped my sexuality and my relationship with my own body. I contracted through my pelvis, and my genitals were distanced as a part of my body, as if they too were bad. I had confused and mixed feelings about genital excitement and anxiety about claiming my penis with excitement and pride.

My experience mobilized an adaptation (a whole way of getting along) meant to protect me from experiencing the pain of rejection and loss of love. However, as I became older, the same adaptation resulted in painful relationships. The loss of my mother's love led to hateful attitudes, first directed toward her, then toward any woman I encountered. Pathways for satisfying needs were aggressively transformed so as not to result in rejection or hate, but the changes that were meant to ensure safety created more difficulties. I have experienced and observed all of this in myself.

In high school, when I learned to masturbate, I did not connect that pleasure with my excitement about girls or with sexual desire for them. There was a disconnect. I took in my experience of my mother's rejection of sticky dandelions, and it carried all the way along to rejection of my desire, the connection between the excitement in my sticky penis and the pretty girl. Inconsolable longing filled in the blank.

CHAPTER 9

Sonny

An Early Death

My brother, Sonny, was a young man of forty-one when he died of Hodgkin's disease. I was thirty-two, in the throes of working on my doctoral dissertation. For the last ten days of his life, our parents, our sister, his wife, and I sat with him in his hospital room in Buffalo, the same hospital where not that many years ago he had been a medical intern.

After the funeral, we were all in shock. I drove my parents to their home in New Jersey, and then returned to my life in Massachusetts. Cambridge felt empty, I felt hollow, and my life dulled down. I was under intense pressure to finish my dissertation. The offer of a best possible job was conditional on finishing by the end of the fall semester. Christmas came and went. I was nowhere near finishing.

I went on hold. I disengaged from the dissertation and drifted into limbo. Two years passed before I re-engaged and completed my project.

Firstborn Son

My parents must have been proud of their firstborn son and named him after his father. Mother liked to say, "I wouldn't let anyone else hold him."

My brother was the family prince, idealized by all of us, especially by my sister and I. He was smart, strong, good-looking, vigorous, and competent. As I grew from baby to little boy, my parents let me drop into the role of little brother and left me there, as if it were my natural home and a sufficient identity. With what I could extract from my connection with my brother, I attempted to fill the vacancy left by my parent's lack of emotional engagement. This had unfortunate consequences for me.

Big Brother

When Sonny was a teenager, he occasionally took me with him to meet friends. He'd take his bike, and I'd ride on the top bar.

"Take deep breaths," he tells me, as he pedals along. He would introduce me as "my kid brother," which made me feel proud. How often he took me along, I don't remember. Following his influence, I got into hiking, birding, and Boy Scouts.

I tended to believe he had capacities I simply didn't have, not thinking I would be able to do what he was doing in another ten years. He could do things like buy a touring bike and ride to Cape Cod; he could finish his Eagle Scout requirements; he could horse around with other big guys and rebuild an old car engine in the back field and get it to run; he could take it upon himself to go to Buffalo, bringing me along, and buy all kinds of equipment for our laboratory in the cellar; he could take it upon himself to buy Dad a full fly fishing kit; all this kind of stuff.

And he could sign up for the US Army Air Force when he came of age during World War II. He trained as a bombardier. Once we visited him in Florida, and he brought me and Dad to his air base. He showed us the small bomber he trained in and encouraged me to go sit in the cockpit and the bubble where the bombardier sat. I was overwhelmed, and I couldn't stop crying. Soon we would be on our way home, leaving him there, and I was frightened for him.

The type of two-engine bomber he trained in was nicknamed "The Flying Coffin." The bombardier sat in a Plexiglas bubble stuck on the nose of the plane, and with an optical telescopic sight, guided the plane down over the target, holding steady in any barrage of anti-aircraft fire and attack planes, until "bombs away." Survival sitting in that bubble hanging out over empty space seemed impossible.

It may have been as terrifying for my brother as it was to me. A photograph from then shows him looking pale and grim. He is in his uniform, flanked by Dad and me. We are outside in the yard. There is snow; it is winter. My expression is strangely distorted, as if I'm crying, but also frightened. He is leaving to go back to duty. Fortunately, this was 1945, the war ended, and he was demobilized without seeing combat.

A Misfortune

That picture, with my strange expression, documents a critical event in my life. One winter night during the Christmas season, while my brother was still in training, he surprised us. That night, as we all slept, he climbed some trellises on to the porch roof, tapped on the bedroom window to wake me, and I let him in. I was thrilled. As he requested, I stayed quiet so he could surprise our parents in the morning. He climbed into bed with me.

He was home a week or ten days. What I experienced during that furlough was unfortunate. It is still a bit sickening to write about. I fell in love with my brother.

The next morning, and for all the mornings he was home, I waited in excitement for him to get up. I felt like we had a special relationship. Of the whole family, I was the one who was special to him. We went cross-country skiing through the woods by the Eighteen Mile Creek, and I was filled with joy and happiness – or so I came to tell myself.

The sad day came when he had to return to duty – the day that picture was taken with me crying at his side. I went along when our father drove him to the train station in the city. Mother was not with us. It was night. On the way home, I sat in the front seat by my father crying, inconsolable. Neither of us spoke.

The next morning, I was still crying. I asked my mother to call school and tell them I wasn't coming.

She said, "No." That was all, just, "No."

I called the school office myself. I said, "I'm not coming today because my brother went back to the army."

It was wartime, soldiers were coming and going. The school secretary was understanding – so different from my mother.

Neither my mother nor my father spoke to me about my grief, and I didn't know how to speak about it to them. I was alone with an indelible bodily impression of a special love and an unresolved grief. That state left me with longing and needing, and – as with anyone falling in love – it carried an erotic charge.

The upshot of this misfortune was that between that surprise visit and my graduation from high school, a period of six years, my emotional life was dominated by, and largely lived through, events centering around my brother.

My development – both sexually and as a person – was in limbo.

The Last Lake

The war ended. To my relief, my brother returned home. I settled back in to being the little brother.

The summer before he started medical school, he made plans for us to take a canoe trip in Canada with two other Boy Scouts and a friend of his. It was an exciting prospect of wilderness adventure and the opportunity to be with Sonny. He arranged for me to go to a nearby summer camp for a couple weeks to learn canoeing.

The outing must have been more stress for him than he had counted on, and it ended on a horrible note. He was not an experienced canoeist, the wooden canoes we had were heavy to portage, and his more experienced friend managed more effectively. Paddling, I didn't have much force, so pushing the canoe fell mostly to him. We straggled behind, together in our canoe.

Paddling for hours every day and portaging with a heavy pack on skimpy rations was more physical effort than I had ever undertaken. Under the weight of my ruck sack, I could not get up from the ground unaided, and I walked bent at a right angle. My brother said little.

Progress was tedious on the open lakes. Starting out in the morning, often under dark clouds, I sat in the bow looking out on a watery vista that stretched on endlessly. The vast sky and dark clouds lowered over the lake. A narrow strip of forested land demarked water from air. With my brother's silence, my inadequate effort, and the tedium, I withdrew into myself, and diffused out into the lines of these infinite spaces.

Paddling through the narrow marshy channels between lakes was a relief. The clear, tannin-stained water was smooth;

we moved through marshy grasses, and the forests felt friendly and near. One afternoon several large bull frogs were sacrificed for a frog-leg appetizer in the evening. One day, using a trolling line, we pulled a beautiful large trout out of the lake and dined well.

I accepted the hard work as the price of being there. We voyaged in a great, nearly primeval, northern forest, where endless chains of lakes could be followed for days. At the end of the day, on rocky outcroppings, we camped and jumped naked into the lake to ease our tired bodies. We drank the lake water and cooked our meal over an open fire. In the evening, the lake was mirrored and smooth. The voices of the wilderness rose around us, moose bellowed, the haunting calls of loons echoed off the lakes, and occasionally the hermit thrush piped his ethereal music.

Swimming naked every day revealed my obvious physical and sexual immaturity in comparison with the other boys. I must have been thirteen, close to fourteen, just before I entered ninth grade. My brother may have had some idea that the trip would help my masculine development.

At the end of the trip, as we paddled down the last lake, he erupted in a crazy rage. He started yelling, "Dig!" to get me to paddle harder. Up to then, he had not so much as hinted at the inadequacy of my paddling. I don't know how long he kept up an unrelenting verbal assault with this one word. All I remember is being on the lake in the bow of the canoe and feeling his yelling coming at me from his place in the stern. I don't recall having a reaction, a feeling, or saying anything to him. I would have been too frightened to be angry with him. What I remember of myself at the time suggests that I was in shock and perhaps – without acknowledging it to myself – was already aware of his anger at me and his view of me as inadequate.

When my brother was dying and I came into his hospital room the first time, he began to cry. I ran over to him. He said, "I wasn't very nice to you on that canoe trip." Our experience that summer had stayed in his mind, as it had mine.

Two years after the canoe trip with my brother, a chance opportunity allowed me to spend a month at a camp in Canada just south of the same wilderness area. I found a good friend. We became practiced with the canoe, ran, and got in shape. With a few others, we took trips and camped. We canoed up to the northern border of the park area, where I had been two years earlier, but traveling further and in fewer days.

Confrontations

Sonny was living at home at the start of his first year in medical school. My ninth-grade classes started the same day as his. After supper that evening, he picked up his big medical texts to go upstairs to study. I picked up my stack of books and homework and started upstairs after him, assuming we were going to study together.

"Oh no!" he barked.

We were not going to be studying together, and we were not going to be involved with each other. He took over "the front room" of the house, and I had our old bedroom, now my room.

I must have been holding the expectation that our "special relationship" would resume, and our closeness was going to pick up from where we left off. Whatever our relationship had been, with one rough, "No!" he ended the love story. I had been living in a pathetic fantasy.

Even after that, for several years I had a sense of waiting when I was around my brother, waiting for the time when our connection would resume as before – or as I had fantasized it. For those years, the fantasy of the special relationship that was like a marriage remained hidden in my inner world.

Sonny met Sally, they married, and lived in Buffalo while he finished medical school. His marriage was a source of unhappiness for my parents. With an insinuating nastiness, his wife drove a wedge between my brother and our parents.

He graduated from medical school, and I graduated from high school the same year. He was twenty-seven and I was seventeen. That summer, after our graduations and before I left for Cornell, Sonny, Sally, her brother, and her parents orchestrated a confrontation with my parents, which for them, as well as myself, had the proportions of tragedy.

They all appeared in a gang one afternoon to stage a showdown. They were full of accusations against my parents, especially my father, for miserably mistreating the doctor-in-the-making – and his wife – by withholding money sufficient for their living expenses.

They did not come in the spirit of appealing to a kindly, loved beneficiary. They were out for blood. Their accusations were merciless. All of them, including my brother, were cruel and demeaning. It was a terrible scene. I was heartsick and watched in horror. The horror that pervaded the scene surely had sources deeper than just financial.

I was left with an awful image from that day: my father on his knees with his face buried in Mother's lap. I was horrified that my strong father who I saw as noble, honest, hardworking, and kind, was reduced to such a state.

Limbo

A few weeks later, on a sunny afternoon at Cornell freshman orientation, I walked across campus in a small group talking with a young woman I had just met. We chatted about our summers, but I did not feel connected to the moment. The recently witnessed family scenario preoccupied me. It had become a shameful family secret. It claimed my allegiance, and already it was keeping me from myself and my own life.

For the years following this event, I watched my parents' life spin around the drama of my brother's life and death. To a large degree, mine did too. At a time when it was crucial to do so, I was not focusing my attention and energies on myself, my own life, and becoming an adult. Through high school and even through college, I was on hold, unawares, as if I were waiting for the moment when I could be the center of my own life.

CHAPTER 10

Without a Compass

Self in Transition

When I applied to college in my senior year of high school, I did not make much out of it, and neither did my parents. We did not talk about it, any more than we talked about anything else. On my own, I took care of the application, writing it out by hand. My school of choice, and the only one I applied to, was the agricultural college at Cornell in Ithaca, New York. I thought I wanted to be an ornithologist, and the agricultural college was home to a prestigious ornithological center. Already having a state scholarship, I knew I would be accepted.

I took care of other preparations as well. I found summer work, and I bought a portable, mechanical typewriter and taught myself to type. When the time came, I packed myself up.

Any excitement I had about taking this next step in life was subdued. It was the next thing I expected myself to do. Vaguely, in the back of my mind, I knew my life would be different, but I accepted that as a matter of fact. I was relieved to leave home. When I look back on my actual departure, I have an image of myself escaping out the front door, pushing against an undercurrent sucking me back into the house to take care of my mother.

A short drive with my parents that first year took me to a new life. I abruptly left the familiar world of my childhood – my safe home on our tree-lined street, my creek and woods. Since I had not learned to talk about my life with my parents or others, I did not have the language or the emotional awareness to name what I was doing "a big step," and of course, I did not have more sophisticated concepts of development and transition.

I had no idea of what it would be like for me, other than more difficult studies. I did not question that just as I had managed much of my life on my own up to then, I would do the same at college. I would be on my own – and alone – when it came to planning studies and any other decision.

Before leaving for college, I made a fateful decision, and as usual I made it without discussing the options with anyone. I made the decision to switch from the agricultural college to the liberal arts college. I learned that I would be expected (as I believed) to live and work on a farm for a summer. The idea of living on a farm with another family triggered fears of being abused, as if the "farmer" would be such a person. It did not occur to me that I might find a friendly environment where a family might enjoy having someone of college age live with them for a few months. Frightened, I arranged to switch to the liberal arts college. In doing so I gave up my plan to be a biologist and ornithologist, the closest ideas I had as to how I wanted my life to be. I was aware of my fear, but I was not aware that it reflected my fear of the world and my fear of men.

Movement Under Self-Duress

I arrived at the university a tightly constrained, anxiously driven young man, frightened of failure, and averse to pleasure and relaxation. I was undeveloped emotionally and physically, weighing 118 pounds at just under five feet, ten inches. My anxiety about measuring up made everything more difficult, and I frequently made things harder than necessary for myself. I had the unfortunate tendency to quickly turn any little thing into something terrible about myself and fall into self-hate. My way of going about studying and learning was inhibited, effortful, and slow. Along with these strains, my head often felt as if I were in a state of shock. Reading should have been easy for me, but it was slow and difficult.

The hodgepodge of experiences growing up in my family with my mother, father, and brother interrupted and confused my sexual development. I was not on good terms with my body; I felt I was unattractive and, in some way, dirty. My familiar longings and loneliness lingered in my inner world, but now, at the university, under pressure to do well, my sexual needs were put on hold, and even dreams and fantasies were dampened.

Self-reproach followed me around campus, a dark pall, out of which rained continuous self-evaluation. Approaching the main entrance to the humanities building, huge classic columns challenged me.

"Do you see how ponderous we are? Do you see the weight we carry, the weight of knowledge?" they asked, reflecting the barely endurable weight I seemed to carry.

I lived with intense stress my first year. I was lonely and had little social contact outside of classes, and I had days of painful depression. Worn down, I was in the infirmary for nine days with viral pneumonia. By the end of the year I was burnt out.

I allowed myself that first year to take Saturday evenings off, see a movie at the student union, and on Sunday mornings, I would take a long walk into the nearby countryside. All the rest of the week was for study.

Work

The possibility of finding meaningful work was what I most wished for myself the first years in college. I had the capacity to put in whatever time was needed and to concentrate; I could "work hard." But my capacity for work had been distorted. I was driven, burdened, inefficient, and I was supposed to do well across the board; but my expectations were unrealistic and overblown. And I did not know what that work might be.

Majoring in philosophy, I lived – and took refuge in – one or another of the libraries much of the time. I developed the intellectual capacity for analytic thinking and the ability to express it in writing during those four years, but I remained undeveloped in being with others, especially women.

As a junior, I signed up for the new honors program in philosophy. The requirement for that year was a research paper on a topic of our choosing. I chose an impossible topic: the concepts of space and time in Einstein's theory of relativity. I knew nothing about it, but apparently felt I had to have a topic of great significance.

I see myself that spring, sitting at my desk in an unbearable state of dread and anxiety. I could not imagine getting through the huge stack of books on my desk. I managed to bear up under the anxiety and pressure, but it was an awful experience. "An ambitious paper," was the instructor's comment. It was good enough to stay in the honors program.

Resources

Although I suffered under this depressive, self-critical stress, I had resources sufficient to allow me to survive and maintain the resilience I needed to keep doing what I believed I needed to do. Also, I had autonomy – the capacity to run my own life. My resources evolved in the context of the stability of my parents' relationship and the safety of my physical home. They are also a product of the freedom I had from my parents' lack of involvement and their limited supervision. My father's character led me to believe in the necessity of hard work, forbearance, and living simply. Watching my mother helped me to learn the necessity of taking care of my body and myself. The relative peacefulness, simplicity, and naturalness of school and village life were a contributing factor, as was my proximity to the creek and woods. Also, I was lucky. Nature gifted me with intelligence, the key to my survival.

These resources allowed me to bear up. They were not recipes for happiness and success; they allowed me to survive. And to some degree they supported some positive traits. I maintained an inner sense of myself that I fell back on when my life was painful. I believed I had the capacity to do meaningful work, find a place in the world, and build a loving relationship. This all lay somewhere in the future, but I had just enough faith in myself to believe that I could move toward those goals. I did pursue them, although most often with the awareness that my movement was slow, always under a duress that I seemed to impose on myself, and frequently my movement stopped almost altogether.

At a Loss

In my college years, what disturbed me most and was my greatest source of unhappiness was being at a loss as to what I wanted to do in life – job, field of study, career – I had no idea. This was a condition I experienced in the core of my being. It was not just a matter of wondering what I might do after college. It was a condition, a state of being that I lived in along with horrible feelings about myself. I experienced it as a major deficit, and it was the source of my greatest grief. It was like missing a sense of who and what I was.

Where a sense of identity should have been, I experienced a cloud of confusion and anxiety. To make it worse, I had not developed the capacity to trust my interests, curiosity, and feelings – that part of my inner compass – which would serve as the basis for working with this dilemma and moving on.

By my sophomore year I decided I would be wise to fulfill premed requirements. I did not want to be a physician, but it was an insurance policy. I started taking the necessary chemistry and physics.

In those days, sitting in lectures, my brain was clouded. Material that should have been easy was blurred, and I could not focus in lectures or on the reading. I managed to get through as if in a fugue state.

My distress only grew. My inner state at that point was a mix of anxiety, confusion, and the all-pervading feeling of being without direction. Proven abilities were no help in this quandary. Making a relationship with a woman I desired in this condition was unimaginable.

This sad state of being was starkly dramatized one day. My friend Barbara had been encouraging me to meet her friend Liz, who was in one of my chemistry courses. I felt drawn to her from brief glimpses and from what Barbara told me.

One day, when the lecture ended, I gathered my books, got up, and as usual, looked in Liz's direction. On this day, she turned toward me and stood a moment looking back at me. I was immobilized. After a moment or two she turned and left the hall. I stood there feeling empty and blank.

I went off to do what I had to do. I must have been numb because I do not remember the feeling in my heart.

Transition Resolved, Transition Begun

By the end of my senior year, the horrible state of being had ameliorated, and I had calmed down. I still did not know what I would do in life, but I was offered the opportunity to continue studying philosophy in the department at Cornell for another two years. Taking advantage of that opportunity gave me a two-year extension on college, which allowed me to become more grounded in my calmer state. I had a corner where I felt somewhat at home and on familiar ground. I felt relatively safe, and, maybe for the first time in my life, began accepting myself with my difficulties and life problems that I did not know how to solve.

Coming into this new state of myself was the important thing that happened for me in those six years. Arriving there was not a result of a conscious plan. At the time, I was not aware of the significance of this development, much less of the process that led up to it. But, nonetheless, I can say that I put in an enormous effort to get there. I just didn't know what the effort was about.

Looking back, I see the process I have been describing and where it brought me. Leaving home and arriving at college was a transition. Suddenly I was having an emotional life that I had not had before, although it did feel like mine, as if I had already been familiar with it. And I was engaged by life problems that I suspected were there, but I had set them aside. Living at home, I was living in a closed-down state, no doubt from shock, fear, and confusion, but also my survival pattern was to lay low and bide my time. I had suppressed the natural growing-up process of attending to myself in the service of becoming a man who had a place in the world. Once at college, it was as if I woke up from some kind of dormancy.

The transition initiated a process that reached its climax in the state of being lost as I described it, and from there, with some connections and a degree of success, I calmed down. The years at college did not lead to my having a life path, at least in an outward way in the social world. The changes and developments involved were inner; they had to do with my self, how I felt about myself and how I saw myself. I was also aware now that I had resources available to me that would aid me in solving my problems in the social world to do with work and relationships. I was in a more developed position from which to find the next step.

The moment of transition and the whole long painful process it set in motion gave me a benchmark from which to map my life. What happened to me and what I experienced in the years at college are almost totally an outgrowth of what had happened to me in the first eighteen years of my life. Similarly, what happened to me subsequently unfolded from who I was at the end of the six years at Cornell. These subsequent experiences also reflect the effects on me of those earlier years. Being able to change and grow depended on the information revealed in all these developments.

PART IV

Vellie

One day, following
pebbles backward carefully
I come upon you
in the clearing.
the trees signal me
"This is it," they whisper
"This is your chance."

– Kathleen Spivack, "figure/ground,"
Swimmer in the Spreading Dawn (1981)

CHAPTER 11

My Life with Men

Opening the View

As I wrote my report, I was engaged in private ongoing self-study, and I wanted to respect and guard that privacy. That, and going at my own pace, gave me a sense of safety. Writing our report is a part of our journey, and it is important to me for that reason. My life as I feel it now is precious, and how I have lived has been my way to freedom.

Writing meaningfully about my life required an in-depth account of my sexual development, which includes important experiences in my sexual life with men. These are sensitive personal matters for me, and all along I have felt a reluctance to publish. I decided to start writing with the trust in myself that I would know what to do if I reached a boundary that I needed to protect.

Transitions to Adult Life

My account in this chapter begins with college years. My earlier experiences with boys that had strong effects on my sexual development are described in other contexts. But their effects are revealed in these transitional experiences.

In college I filled my days with activities that made me part of various groups, but I was hesitant and restrained around young men. Nonetheless, I fell in love in my third year with a ministerial student at a nearby college. At the same time, I did not identify that what I was experiencing was falling in love, nor was I able to. For some weeks we would talk on the phone every day, and we were often together on the weekends, usually with a group of friends.

One evening we drove to a little park where college students could go safely. We had never had a private time before. We got out of the car and I felt that we were in a couple as we walked. Everything with him had always gone easily; I felt I had a boyfriend.

We stopped and kissed, and I remember this kiss. I responded with feeling. My body moved spontaneously with desire, and I naturally pressed my pelvis against him. At that time in my life, I didn't know that what I was experiencing and feeling is called "desire," and I had not known that my feelings for him meant I had fallen in love. I do not remember the rest of that evening, but when we met the next day, he was cool and distant. This confused and disturbed me. He didn't call me again, and we didn't meet again.

When I thought back on that evening and remembered his coldness the next day, the only way I could resolve my confusion and pain was to believe that I should not have kissed him with such strong feelings, and that his rejection was my fault. I had a few dates with other students after that, but I made sure I did not trust my strong feelings again. I did not talk with anyone about my life and my struggles. No one in the family knew about this important development in my life. I was on my own.

After graduating with my nursing degree, I went to Denver for a year. I became friends with some of the young men in their third year of medical school. These young men were charmed by my Southern accent and manner, but they soon realized I was immature when it came to dating. However, I still had the experience of having attention as a young woman and having fun with the young men without the challenge of dating and confronting the possibility of sex. But I began to realize how different I was from my friends and had some awareness of a problem.

Luke

Returning to Louisiana from Denver as a twenty-two-year-old, I immediately started to work at the hospital where I had trained as a student nurse. I lived with my parents and agreed to help them pay off their debts. My life at this time was going from home to work, and back. Most of my friends were married, the doctors and nurses at the hospital all had families, and I felt alone in a little pocket. I did not know what I wanted to do about marriage and family. I had hardly dated, and I had never experienced a long-term relationship.

In this ambiguous state, I met Luke. I was with him for two years. During most of that time we were engaged to be married, and I wore the ring he gave me. In the beginning, I felt I was like other young women I knew, and I would do what they – my friends and my sisters – had done: be engaged, get married, and start a family – the dream of many young women.

I had my first sexual experience with Luke. I was twenty-three. At the initiation of our sexual life together, I was excited, and I experienced orgasms. Although I grew up believing that a good Baptist girl did not have sex outside of marriage, my initial sexual experiences with him felt natural. The thought I was doing something wrong did not occur to me.

Although my sexual life began, I do not recall feelings of intimacy or love. I did not have the kind of feelings that I had had with the ministerial student. I was caught up in the excitement of being engaged, doing what everybody did, and being with this dramatic young man. But our relationship never felt quite real to me. I did not know what "real" might be. I observed other couples, including my sisters, but what I saw did not offer me any insights about what they might be experiencing that was different from what I was experiencing with Luke.

Our relationship quickly changed after just a month. Luke took it upon himself to comment that he knew my orgasmic response was a sign of my being "sexually experienced." I was shocked. In addition to throwing me into a shocked state, he put a negative stamp on our sex and made it bad – made me bad.

Also, he kept telling me about his sexual life, informing me about the women he had been with. He had met many accessible young women because he was a race car driver for a wealthy family in Atlanta who owned these expensive race cars – an impressive, unusual activity. I had already been impressed by seeing him as a brilliant student at a great university.

After these experiences in the first couple of months of our relationship, I stopped having sexual feelings with him. I often found myself crying without knowing why, and these episodes continued for the rest of our time together, another year or more. I felt my unhappiness must be connected to my being with him in some way, but I was more inclined to believe that any shortcomings in the relationship were because I was not pretty enough, not outgoing enough, and not intelligent enough – all of those things and more. Those were the problems, I thought.

In later years, when I had a deeper knowledge of myself, I understood that his remark about my sexuality had penetrated my inner world and threatened to reveal my repressed sexual secrets. This makes it understandable that I would be terribly upset and be sent into shock.

Over the two years I was engaged, many experiences revealed my lack of development. I certainly lacked self-agency. I did not have sufficient awareness of myself or of the world to take care of myself, act for myself, and make my own decisions. Luke became more and more dominating around many details of our life as a couple, even telling me where I should work. I experienced him as intelligent, talented, and successful – qualities that I knew I wanted in the man that I would spend my life with. I did not see beyond my fantasy of who he was. But still, we did have times of fun and exciting adventures. He always conveyed a lively, dramatic excitement that kept me engaged and energized.

After two years, he ended our engagement, and he asked for the ring back. I readily agreed. I felt relieved. Most of the unhappiness I experienced was from thinking it was all my fault and that I was not enough. I hurt and I cried, but I was not experiencing the terrible pain of loss.

When our engagement ended, I decided I wanted to live and work in a city in the Midwest. After all, I had worked in Denver for a year after graduating from college, which had been exciting, and I had learned more about the world. I talked with other nurses who had traveled, and their stories sounded like great adventures. I thought about what I wanted, did research, and decided on Chicago.

Young Doctor

I was on my way in a few weeks. With my car packed, I started out ready to drive to Chicago. Less than a mile from my parents' house, I stopped to let some puppies go across the road. A young man going fast ran into the back of my car. I was not hurt, but my car was too damaged to drive.

I had a date for starting work, so I made arrangements to have my car repaired and took the train to Chicago. It was an exciting trip for me. When I arrived at Union Station, I could not believe the activity and what I interpreted as sophistication in the way people hailed taxis. So I watched and waited with my small trunk and a couple of suitcases until all the taxis were gone, except for one. That driver came over to me, took my trunk and suitcases, and drove me to the residence at the hospital where I was to work.

In the first weeks of work, I met a fourth-year medical student. He invited me to parties, movies, and football games. I enjoyed having a dating life. I started having fun. Our relationship developed and we were sexual. He made a comment I never forgot. He said, "This is what a perfect woman's body looks like." I remember his comment because it was what I needed to hear. Within myself, I understood him to say, "*You are a woman.*" My identity as a woman was validated. I felt his capacity to enjoy and care for a woman. I was impressed I could feel that because I had not experienced this capacity in Luke.

During the Christmas holidays I returned to Louisiana to retrieve my repaired car. We planned that on the way back to Chicago I would spend New Year's Eve at his family home, where I would meet his mother and friends. He planned a fun ice-skating party with his friends.

The trip to his house turned out to be stressful. My father had decided he would drive with me the first day, so most of that day was spent in the car with him. I left him at the train station in Memphis for his return to Louisiana. The next day, New Year's Eve, I encountered a snowstorm. I put my car in a garage and spent another night in a hotel. After roads were cleared New Year's Day, with few directions, I managed to find my way to his house (we had no GPS then).

I was anxious by the time I arrived, and I sensed tension between my friend and his mother, so I had little contact with her. I did not know what was causing the tension between them, but later he indicated she did not want him to be involved with someone while still in medical school. Apparently, inviting me to his home to meet the family and friends suggested to her that the relationship was more important than she would like it to be.

Our relationship ended after another month or so. I do not remember feeling loss or pain about the ending. I remember a confused acceptance.

Dan

A few months after that relationship ended, I went with my roommate to a party. I met Dan, who was maybe ten years older and a psychiatric resident at my hospital. I came to know Dan as a kind man. He was a good person altogether. I felt safe with him and valued as a woman. We started our caring sexual relationship that lasted about a year.

Dan came to love me, and the sad part is that the evening he started talking about marriage, I found myself saying, "But I am not ready. I want to go out with others." This had not been in my mind, but at that moment, that is what I said. I remember his expression. He was clearly hurt. I recall him saying, "But I thought if you love someone you would only want to be with him?"

As I look back, I realize how cold and heartless I was. What I also see is my fear and numb state. I was not in contact with my feelings at that moment. Possibly I feared losing my freedom, but there were deeper sources for that fear. Our relationship soon ended, but we stayed friends and sometimes lovers for another twenty years. We remained friends until he died.

Carlos

Following the end of my relationship with Dan, I met a medical resident, Carlos, who was from Spain. We began dating, and he became an important person in my life. I did not make a commitment to him and dated other men, as I had wanted to.

Around the end of my second year in Chicago, my father was diagnosed with stage four colon cancer. Without hesitation, I left my work and life in Chicago and took a job at the VA hospital in New Orleans so I could oversee his treatment (I will discuss this decision later).

Carlos asked if we could continue seeing each other, and he would come to New Orleans for weekends or for a week when possible. He came often for more than a year. We tried to get to know each other to see if our relationship would last if I went to Spain with him, or if he came back to the States later. With the possibility of going to Spain in mind, I attempted some preparations and took Spanish classes. I was not able to stay with the planning.

After he left to return to Spain. I had a terrible time with vertigo, even spending a couple of days in a hospital. He thought my reaction was due to his leaving me. Years later I learned that vertigo could be my way of reacting to loss.

As the months passed, our interest waned, and our letters diminished in quality and number. Our contact ended without my having strong feelings. I had already experienced the loss in the only way I could. This was 1965–1966.

Ben, 1967

In Boston I settled into a job teaching nursing students and found a nice apartment near my work. I met Ben at a party within the first year there. He was a physicist, brilliant, quiet, and kind. We started a relationship that lasted for almost twelve years. I do not remember ever saying to him that I loved him, although here again was someone who treated me wonderfully.

As a young woman, now age thirty, my way of life in this period felt easy and how I wanted my life to be. A man was in my life who I enjoyed and who wanted to be with me. I had matured into more awareness of myself, and I felt confident I was doing what I wanted to be doing. I found a place in Cambridge I believed could become my home and where I could live my life. The South was no longer my home.

Ben and I enjoyed life together in Cambridge, and on weekends we often went hiking or skiing in the mountains. We would be together only on weekends or holidays. This was all I could do; we never lived together. I knew I needed to manage my energy and time spent with others, and I could not cope with working and being with Ben during the week.

Ben was strongly invested in his involvement with me during our first two years. However, when he even hinted that he was thinking of us as a committed couple, I would withdraw and become distant. I was aware he felt hurt and puzzled, but I did not and could not respond. With my reaction to his hints, there was a subtle break in our relationship. But he continued to offer me an arrangement I could cope with.

Our third year marked a further attenuation of our involvement. I went to Europe for five months, and when I returned Ben went to Israel for six months. This shift in our involvement suited me. I did not feel the threat of commitment. And I maintained my feeling of freedom.

By the time he returned from abroad, we no longer assumed we would be together every weekend. I would go off on my own some weekends or even for a week. Possibly he did the same. Even with this arrangement, I still held the sense of our being together, and apparently, he did too.

As more years went by, my relationship with Ben became more tenuous and ambiguous. The last evening I spent with him, my emotions broke through, and there was no stopping them. A few months earlier, we had had a crisis that had been painful for both of us. We continued being together without talking about the crisis and sharing our pain.

That last evening, we had just sat down to eat supper at his apartment. He said something or something happened – as if it were waiting to happen – and I burst into tears. My crying was frantic. I got up and ran to get my coat, feeling I had to leave. He tried to help me, but I kept crying, ran to my car, and drove home. It was as if my inner world, with all my pain, had broken through.

CHAPTER 12

Phil Enters My Life

If I am I because I am I, and you are you because you are you, then I am I and you are you. But if I am I because you are you, and you are you because I am I, then I am not I, and you are not you.

– Attrib. R. Simhah Bunim (cited in Michael Rosen, *The Quest for Authenticity*, 2008)

First Encounters

I had been teaching nursing at one of the Boston hospitals, but I was not comfortable being a teacher. I decided to pursue my interest in psychology. I left my job in the school of nursing and arranged for a National Institute of Mental Health (NIMH) grant to study community mental health offered by a program at Boston State Hospital; this was for the year 1969–1970.

During my year on the grant, I attended many seminars, and I first saw Phil at one of them. A large group attended, and we all sat around a small stage, except for one man who quietly walked back and forth around the room without disturbing the proceedings. He was an interesting looking person, obviously very attentive and serious. I did not know who he was and did not attempt to meet him.

At just this time, my clinical supervisor had started talking to me about meeting a man she liked who had become a new friend of hers, and she thought we should meet. She thought we were similar in some way. I told her I was not interested, since I was in a relationship, but she continued to mention him. At the same time, she was telling Phil about me. But he was also in a relationship.

Finally, sometime in the spring, Phil called me. When he arrived at my door, I realized he was the man I had noticed at the seminar, so I was very curious and excited to meet him. My supervisor and friend had talked about him for several months, so I felt I knew him. I think we went out to dinner, and then – almost automatically – we went to his apartment. Our lovemaking was exciting.

After that night, we met now and then, sometimes talked on the telephone, and became friends. For me, Phil was a friend with whom I had a warm and easy sexual connection. I responded to him with desire, which was not always a part of my sexual response. I enjoyed being able to make love without the entanglement of a "relationship." I did not feel it was a problem in my ongoing relationship. Apparently, I was free to feel more if I were *not* in a relationship.

I remember saying that we were good for each other, because we could talk about our relationships and get encouragement and support for our difficulties. Phil especially needed someone he could talk to. I was concerned for him in his anguish about breaking up with his woman, and I helped him plan an extended trip to Esalen. When he returned, we continued our easy ongoing friendship, with only occasional evenings together.

I told myself I was not in a relationship with Phil, but something happened that revealed part of me felt otherwise. We met for lunch and he told me he had met a woman he wanted to be with, and he wanted to stay friends, but he would only be sexual within his new relationship. I remember riding home on my bicycle from Harvard Square and feeling sad. My good friend came by later that day and found me crying. Crying about loss was new to me.

We continued a friendship as colleagues, and later we shared offices with two others, so we saw each other during the week. I continued to feel comfortable and at ease with Phil.

Then It Got Serious

Ten years after I first met Phil, I discovered how sexually excited I could be and how difficult an intimate relationship could be for me. A few months after Ben and I made a final separation, I met with Phil for lunch at my condo to go over plans for our offices. After he left, I realized how much I liked him and how I felt the excitement once again being with him. He had ended the relationship he had been in for several years, so I called him. I did not hesitate to let him know I was feeling my sexual excitement. We agreed to meet that evening at my condo.

I always thought I wanted to marry and have a family, but later. That day I called Phil, I was forty-three, and it was indeed later. My conscious wish to see him was not based on ideas about marriage or even a committed relationship. I still needed time by myself to be free and to self-regulate. I had ended the long-time relationship and felt the pure pleasure of freedom. I had my community of friends and my work, so I was not worrying about practical matters when I called.

Phil and I started on our journey. Being together energized me on all levels of my being, and I started feeling more alive. I needed to balance my wish to be with Phil and my needs to be alone and feel free. I had to accommodate myself to Phil's different ways of coming and going that resulted from his ambiguity about what he wanted.

As it worked out, we were together for quite a bit of the week pretty much from the start. We worked in the same office space two days a week, and it was convenient and comfortable for both of us for him to stay two nights a week with me at my condo. On Saturday, I would pack up myself and my dog and join Phil at his home in Pepperell, and despite – or maybe along with – our various ups and downs, I felt comfortable and easy with our fluid arrangements.

After four years of being together on this schedule, I moved out to Pepperell to be with Phil and live with him there. This time, besides bringing along my little dog, I also brought my cat, Kitty Girl – so we were serious. Even before that, we felt closer and wanted to be together more. I had started going out to Pepperell on Friday afternoon, and sometimes stayed until Monday morning. We still had Monday and Tuesday evenings at my condo, and I had two to three days alone.

Moving in with Phil was a big step for me. From early on, I had to limit my work hours to manage our increased contact. Soon, I made our relationship my priority. When I moved out to Pepperell, I cut back even more on my work hours.

My Obstacles to Love

We had a strong wish to be together and found it a great pleasure. I started experiencing longings for the safety and security of feeling love, longings that were new to me. But from the start we regularly and frequently experienced episodes of discord, pain, and turmoil. My heart was full of feelings, but I was not able to sustain my love. With the slightest hint of conflict or criticism, or even if Phil had a difficult feeling that did not involve me, I became frightened and would withdraw in an attempt to find safety in a quiet space.

As yet I did not realize how my childhood and adolescent development put the love I longed for out of reach. I held hidden fear, anger, and distrust of my father and men. When I say hidden, I mean I was unaware of these feelings. I could not allow a relationship to deepen to a level of strong sexual, loving intimacy. This inner dynamic was deeply hidden, a secret even from myself.

Anger and fear were not the only obstacles to love I encountered. Another inner-world dynamic was just as profound. Through talks with Phil, I arrived at a bodily awareness of a "badness" in me. Once I was in touch with it, I felt that it had been there forever. I did not feel bad because of something; it was not "because of" anything. It was simply there; it was my condition.

I longed to be a soft, loving, sexual woman with the capacity to feel and be intimate. As I opened to more feeling, I was dismayed to encounter the obstacles to my goals. To change, I had to confront my fears, my terror, my anger, and my dissociation, again and again in my daily life.

Resisting

By avoiding deeper intimacy in my relationships, I was not moving towards finding the love that I longed for. My experience of love and being respected in my childhood had not been sufficient for the development of the self-love that would lead to finding love with another. My dedication to my psychotherapy was an attempt to make up for that deficit.

With Phil, self-protection was quickly mobilized. If he tried to get me to talk with him about myself or what I was feeling during even a minor conflict, I felt pressured and frightened. I used several ways to ward him off. I would cry and say, "I don't know" – which was true. If he persisted in demanding contact, I upped the ante into more active self-protection, and I used my anger to keep him at a distance. I felt I must always defend myself. My resistance continued in the face of Phil's persistent efforts to ask for connection and tell him what was going on (which I really did not know).

His insistence and my resistance sometimes led to frantic escalation. In desperation, I wanted to escape. I could hear a scream that would come from deep inside me, make gestures towards injuring myself, and worst of all, feel a wish to die, which seemed my only out. I felt a safety in allowing myself to go to these extremes. I knew I had ego strength never to cross a line, and the extremes were making me aware of the deeper feelings I was living with.

I felt a terrible need to get away, get alone, live alone. Sometimes I would go to my small room downstairs or go into the woods and hide under my welcoming hemlock tree, anything to get away, until I could calm down. I never imagined being in an intimate relationship would provoke such intense feelings and what I considered strange behavior. Out of such experiences I came to understand why I had never considered living with a man or getting married.

After going through one of these episodes, as I started calling them, we would re-establish contact and renew our connection, each time believing that we had resolved the difficulty, and now we could be safe and happy. The painful reality was that this would last only a day or maybe a week or two before I would once again be triggered, and we would be in another episode.

There were times when I could stay grounded enough to say to Phil, "Can't we at least be friendly?" or I could sometimes find a way through cooking a good meal or doing something with loving kindness that would allow me to hold the sense of our connection. Sometimes Phil could help me find the exit (as I would say) from my traumatized, tortured experience. We would both feel relieved and know we had coped with something especially important and learned more about ourselves.

Coming Alive

Traumatic shock frozen in my body was the basis for these repetitive, horrible episodes. They showed me that if I was going to remain in this intimate relationship, I would have to make changes. I started the long journey of learning about myself. Slowly but surely my frozenness melted, and I softened. As I softened, I came to feel more comfortable in my own body. I began experiencing the promise of longed-for changes.

Before I began my life in Boston, and for some years thereafter, I had not been in touch with my traumatized self. As I developed, I came to feel my depression and sadness, which others had seen all along. When Prozac became available, I got a prescription and used it for a year. After a week or two, I would wake up in the morning feeling the pleasure of being alive, which was so distinctly different from the depressive state.

Prozac let me feel what it was like not to be depressed. Once again, I had a normal, healthy body feeling such as I had experienced as a young child. It was as if my body regained the knowledge or awakened the imprint of a healthy feeling. And now, when I lost my good feeling, that imprint helped me regain it even after I stopped the Prozac.

Also, I met Dr. K, an endocrinologist who knew how to

keep me regulated and safe on hormone-replacement therapy. That regimen added to the sense of emotional stability, which was a great help.

Another drug that was beneficial for regaining my good feelings was MDMA (Ecstasy). I took it for the first time one lovely, sunny afternoon in Pepperell. As I lay on the bed waiting for the effect, I began to feel something that to this day is difficult to describe. My words then to Phil were, "I did not know a human could feel so wonderful."

I remember a soft, relaxed, sweet, beautiful feeling in my body, a feeling of pure pleasure. The feelings came from within me; they were not due to any external factor such as being with Phil or the sunny day. What I experienced was my body state. Even though the intensity of these feelings faded, I have never lost the bodily impression of that state. That afternoon we talked and were open and honest in ways I did not know could be possible between two people. This experience of talking with safety was a healing experience.

On another sunny day when I took MDMA for the second time, we went out walking, and I found myself feeling pure joy. I literally jumped for joy. I felt a letting go or release in my feet and ankles, and that created the jump. That state of joy and the jump came out of my body spontaneously. Now, more than thirty years later, I know for a certainty that these states are revelations of how wonderful a human can feel. Afterwards they were not regular ongoing experiences in my daily life, but the impressions they left have a positive influence in how I feel day to day.

In later years, I was sometimes taken to wonderful peaks of experience by MDMA or LSD. Once on MDMA, I felt the wonder of being female and feeling happy as a woman, an experience that was particularly important on my healing journey.

One time on LSD, I sat out on our porch in Pepperell and, looking out at the world around me, I saw the absolute beauty of the natural world with the clear eyes I may have had as a child. There were many times on LSD or MDMA when I could see such beauty and feel the joy of being alive. Once I listened to Bach and could hear the music with an openness to the wonder I had not experienced before.

These experiences are part of my journey. When the state of the body-self that I describe as "how wonderful a human can feel" does appear, even in a lesser form, it is a joyful, healing experience. It supports the journey – which Phil and I continue.

PART V

Phil

What is meant by unification of the soul would be thoroughly misunderstood if "soul" were taken to mean anything but the whole man, body and spirit together. The soul is not really united unless all bodily energies, all the limbs of the body are united.

– Martin Buber, *The Way of Man: According to the Teachings of Hasidism* (1966)

CHAPTER 13

A Brief History of Nonmarriage

Thirty-Two Years

A woman who knew me from years past asked how long Vellie and I had been together.

I replied, "Thirty-two years."

"Thirty-two years! That's a long time! We thought you'd never get married."

Knowing me from those years, she could hardly have thought otherwise. She did not know I also longed for just that.

Debbie

The summer after I graduated from Cornell, I stayed in Ithaca to enjoy myself and complete a course. It was hot, I was on the third floor, so my door was always open. One day Debbie walked into my room. I hadn't seen her before, but she also had just graduated and was staying in the same house. Intimacy bloomed in a heartbeat.

One day soon after meeting, we were in the country and took a path towards a nearby lake. We paused, and we kissed. I was literally knocked off my feet and sat down right there.

Later she asked me why I sat down, but I didn't have an answer. It was not my first kiss, but it was the first with passion.

Led by her, I experienced sexual love for the first time. She had a natural, comfortable sexual maturity and health. Being with her and feeling so happy was a new kind of experience for me – like a blessing.

We did not have much time together. She was going to England to work and was leaving soon. I had a last sorrowful visit with her.

The Philosophy Department offered me an assistantship for the next year, so I stayed in Ithaca. My heart ached for Debbie, and I was sad and lonely that fall. This was the period of the Korean Conflict, and my academic year was interrupted by a military obligation. I had expected to be in the army for two years, but the conflict ended, and I was discharged.

When the Philosophy Department offered me a fellowship for the next year, I returned to Ithaca. I did some good work in philosophy, but I still missed Debbie, and I had another sad, lonely year. That spring, she visited the campus with the man she had met in England whom she was going to marry.

Intermittently over the next few years, feelings of loss and of missing her washed through me. A few years later, I ran into the couple who were her good friends, and I asked about her.

"You let her go," they said.

I had. What they said left me miserable. I was not ready for a relationship with a healthy young woman who was ready for marriage and children.

Debbie had stepped into my heart just as easily as she first stepped through the open door to my room and said, "Hi." She was ensconced there the first time we kissed. I was not ready to claim her, and I was not able to accept a sad farewell and move on.

Shirley

Debbie's departure left me in a state of lingering sorrow. Had a good angel guided me, I would have taken counsel with myself and attended to my sorrows. The angel was not in attendance. I was in a vulnerable position, without knowing how to take care of myself or what I needed.

With all good intentions, my friend Barbara encouraged Shirley and me to meet. I was in no state to embark on a new relationship, but I felt lonely, mournful, and missed physical intimacy. Shirley liked me, wanted to build a relationship, and offered herself sweetly and freely. I knew I would not recreate the happiness I felt with Debbie, but I pushed aside such thoughts.

As gentle, loving and caring a person as Shirley was, as giving and interested sexually, I was not able to make the connection. Where sex came easily with Debbie, with Shirley, I struggled. We were together a couple of years. She saw that I was troubled, but she didn't want to send me away and get on with someone who was ready. Moodily I lingered, irritable, ambivalent, dissatisfied, and needing to get free.

At the end of my fellowship year in the Cornell Philosophy Department I left Ithaca with no plans in mind. My father was working in New York City, so for the summer I stayed in my parents' apartment. At a loss, I took a job in an insurance company. With my sister's help, I set myself up in an apartment in Newark. The job was unbearable for me, and as planned, after six tedious months, I liberated myself. I found a small room in a boarding house in New York City on the West Side, near Riverside Drive. I did not make the mistake of getting another job. For the first time in my life, I was free from institutional life in any form.

The Beatnik

I identified with the beatniks – their restlessness, need for freedom, sexual joy, and openness. I was happy living marginally and enjoyed watching city life. I had saved a little money, and my mother at this time began sending me a modest check every month, a caring deed she never spoke of and continued through graduate school.

I sold ice cream from a pushcart; I delivered packages in the garment district by hand truck. Day and night I prowled the city, often ending up in Harlem. I observed the African American women and Latinas on the streets and in the bars, and occasionally I paid for their services.

Beatnik life suited me. I cooked in my tiny room on a two-burner gas top, traveled around the city, went to museums, read, and practiced drawing. I took courses in psychology at City College of New York. I especially liked a course in psychoanalytic theory with Martha Wolfenstein. For her course I wrote a psychoanalytic study of Kafka, which was well received.

With urging from my brother, I found a therapist in New York. I was excited by the therapy process, and with his support, I let Shirley go.

At City College, I met Betty. Once again, I was sexually happy. She could have been a life partner. She was going to graduate school in Massachusetts; she was fun, smart and – compared with myself – mature. Thoughts of commitment did not cross my mind.

I found an interesting job as a research assistant at the New York State Psychiatric Institute at Columbia University. Two sweet affairs began there. It was a happy time. I applied to graduate schools, and Harvard offered me a full university fellowship – an offer way too good to turn down.

Harvard and Cambridge: Ages Twenty-Six to Forty-Six

Twenty life-packed years lay between the fall of 1959 (when I began graduate studies, age twenty-six) and spring 1980, age forty-six (when Vellie and I got together).

At Cornell I struggled with brain shock, depression, and inner disturbance. Being in graduate school, back in academia, triggered my anxiety, insecurity, and self-punitiveness. At the same time, I once again felt driven to find my "mission" and do great things. Although I was not as overwhelmed as I had been earlier, my ability to read and learn were still hampered.

My program took four academic years plus a year's internship. When I wrote my dissertation proposal, I formulated questions that I hardly understood, much less knew how to go about answering. My faculty advisers signed on to it, and I was on my own.

That project took me another four years to complete. Twice outstanding academic appointments were withheld because of the unfinished dissertation. When I did finish, Robert N. Bellah, one of my advisers and world renown scholar in the sociology of religion, said, "It is the best work in the psychology of religion since William James." I didn't know what to do with that kind of praise, but I was happy and proud when my book was published.

Through these twenty years, when I was not engaged body and soul in a love relationship, I was actively dating and seeking one. Some of these relationships were nonmarriage marriages. They were marriage-like in terms of duration (five or more years); they were monogamous, intimate, and I was immersed in our mutual life as a couple.

Margaret

After a lonely first year in Cambridge, I met Margaret. One day, leaving the little house used by the Clinical Psychology Department, I encountered a young woman who was looking at me, laughing nervously with excited recognition, and dancing about in an engaging way. As it turned out, she was the roommate of a woman with whom I had a romance just the year before in New York City. Evidently, this did not put her off, because we began to date.

We were together for almost five years. This was her first relationship. For me as well, Margaret was the first woman with whom I consistently maintained my connection over a period of years. As time went on, her family treated us as if we were a couple soon to be married. As odd as it may seem, I never gave it a thought.

I had fun with Margaret. She wasn't working very much or going to school, and she had a light-hearted approach to life. She had a keen eye aesthetically and for people, and she talked with an amused musical laugh. Being with her relieved the tedium of studies and writing papers, and we spent nights together and made love.

With Margaret, I learned to storm. She was excitable and easily offended. Then she was quick to bring me down a peg with some scratchy observation, and one thing led to another. We had screaming matches, something new to me. Irritability calmed, affection returned, and we made love.

For those few years we were together, she was a constant part of my daily life. I was fond of her, and I became attached. Separating was painful and sad. I do not recall how we decided to separate, but inevitably we did. For a few weeks, I sat in my apartment drinking whiskey at night and crying; I hurt and felt sorry for myself.

Trying to visualize the few years following that separation, I encounter a blurry impression, not chaotic, but not particularly focused. My brother died during this period, aged only forty-one. Cambridge felt barren and empty after being with him in his last days.

I gained experience as a psychologist, dated, and lived my life, but I was not living with much verve. A convenient job at the new Boston branch of the University of Massachusetts fell into my lap.

Clare

She showed up in one of my classes, immediately catching my attention. She was lovely. She was Chinese, had recently come to America from Macau, and was a bit older. She dropped my course. I bumped into her later and asked her out. I was eager to see her again, and soon we were seeing each other regularly. Despite her apparent disinterest in my class, we got along together in an easy enjoyable way. I was enchanted with her beauty and our sexual pleasure. We were together for five years.

We did not live together, but we were together for most nights and on weekends. Our lives entwined. I experienced times of genuine happiness with her. Pictures she took of me from one summer when I rented a cottage on a small lake near Cambridge show me looking happy and at ease. We rarely argued or fought, although she may have been angry more often than I knew. I loved her and cared about her.

I was still boondoggling along with my dissertation. At the end of my first year at U Mass, I began to worry that I would be hanging around Cambridge for years, never finishing my degree. I mobilized myself, found the therapist I needed to give me a nudge, and I finished. Clare and I were together that spring when I received my degree and when I started working on my book manuscript.

Marriage and family did not occur to me. Oddly enough, at the same time, I felt she was my wife. I was peculiarly oblivious of her earnest wish that we marry and have a family. At one point we saw a couple's therapist.

She said, "I want to get married."

I had a strange reaction: I was horrified and felt betrayed!

That event probably marked the start of the period when I became more troubled. I was taken over by a combination of passion and chaotic disturbance that I was unable to manage. Day after day I lived in anguished preoccupation and tortured unhappiness that went on and on. I had little grasp of what was happening to me. But it went on for the best part of two years.

I met professional responsibilities, and I got to where I was supposed to go. I took care of myself, and I looked okay. But my inner world was in a turmoil and out of control. Unless distracted by working with colleagues or patients, I swam in my preoccupations about her.

I was invaded by the feeling that I was suffering miserably because of Clare – supposedly, from her lack of love, her not caring, her abandonment. None of this was true. I was not accusatory or suspicious. That state just lived in me. It was my reality and being in contact with the real person did not change it for me. I had never lived through anything like it.

For two years I accomplished nothing. My dissertation had been accepted for publication, and my main task was to prepare the manuscript. I could not do a thing with it. It no longer seemed like mine. I sat in my small office day after day doing nothing; it was tedious and painful.

A few close friends knew I was having difficulty and was unhappy, but no one knew what I was going through. One day a woman friend told me she did not want to hear any more about Clare, and I had a glimpse of what a state I was in.

We broke off for a period, reunited, but I left. I found an escape. I did not have the wherewithal to talk with her about what was happening to me or find out what was happening for her. In the end, I left town.

I was working part-time at the Adolescent Service at Boston State Hospital. I arranged to be in residence at the Esalen Institute in California for three months and asked for leave from my job.

Driving across country from Massachusetts to California by myself was nightmarish, the heart of darkness. Beyond forlorn, I felt driven down into some wretched purgatory.

I had been crazy about Clare. But that was just it. I was in love with her. Being in love so deeply had conjured a turmoil in me, and I did know what it all was or what it meant.

For three months I took asylum at Esalen. My attention shifted away from Clare. I calmed down. Going through the devastation of the actual separation brought me back to myself. Once again, I felt freedom and breath. I was also enlivened and enlightened by the new work in therapy and growth work.

Back east Vellie was the first person I called. With my friend Myron Sharaf, we went to see the Makavejev film, *Mysteries of the Organism*, about Wilhelm Reich. I had concluded that my personal experience at Esalen could be best understood in the light of Reich's work. We organized "The Tuesday Group" – myself, Vellie, Myron, my dear friend Ildri Ginn, and other friends. Our intention was to supervise each other in learning Reichian therapy. We soon discovered we needed to focus on our own personal issues and turned the group into a self-led therapy group. For several years, I felt at home in this group, and it supported my development as a therapist.

Kaelin

Meeting Kaelin came about through a quixotic turn of events. I was invited to talk to the Psychiatry Department at Tufts New England Medical Center about my Esalen experience. Naively, I shared my excitement with this august, conservative group.

I offered to demonstrate gestalt therapy. A cute, young nurse volunteered. She had an infectious, mischievous grin, and I became befuddled. I doubt there was much demonstrating; embarrassment mercifully limits my recall. My friend, Andy Morrison, who invited me, was amused, but I do not think the senior psychiatrists were.

I was taken by this breath of fresh air and good spirits. Andy found out where I could reach her, and we spent the next seven years together. Her name was Kaelin.

When I bought a house for us, her name was on the deeds. Nonetheless, when she asked me if I was going to marry her, I said, "No!" I said it in a mean way, as if I were saying, "Don't be ridiculous." At the end of that seven years, she wisely arranged a separation.

Kaelin was full of energy, sexual, smart, and enterprising, and during our time together, she trained in professional massage and yoga, became a runner, and developed personally. She was twenty-three when I met her; I was forty.

With Kaelin – regretfully – I was paternalistic, sometimes mean, and often cold. I yelled and got angry for nothing. At the same time, I needed her and relied on her. When I allowed myself, I felt close and appreciative, and we had fun together. I am sad for my rough behavior with her; she deserved nothing but warmth and kindness. But she flourished and developed in those years and did not take my hatred into herself. A year after she separated from me, she married and began her family.

A Failure to Learn

My history with Kaelin shows me acting with a peculiar obliviousness. For the two chaotic years prior to meeting Kaelin I had been submerged in my inner world, managing to function just well enough to hold on to my work life. I had just spent three months at Esalen in recovery and grieving Clare. I calmed down and came back to myself. But I returned east and picked up from where I had been derailed two years earlier. I set about seeking another nonmarriage marriage without allowing myself the time I needed to live with myself, develop, and learn.

Getting together with Kaelin, I overrode the weak voice of my better judgment, and encouraged myself to believe that I was in love and that all was well. At least I was not going crazy again. I also knew that I was not unreservedly with her, as I had been with Clare.

When I separated from Kaelin, I was no longer able to outpace my past. Being netted in free fall by my connection with Vellie not only saved my life, it was another transition point. Being with her gave me the ground on which I was able to start getting to grips with myself.

A Variegated Life

Arriving in Cambridge to begin graduate school at age twenty-six was another transition point, like arriving at college, age eighteen. I had developed, learned, and become stronger as a person, but at the same time, beginning graduate school had the same effect on me as starting college. I was confronted with myself, my conflicts, and disturbances, and my resources were strained.

I arrived in Cambridge with mixed feelings. My goals were vague, other than wanting to acquire skills and credentials that would allow me to establish myself in the world. I acted as if this outcome would take care of itself if I acquired a PhD. But in the meantime, I would again be submitting myself to demanding expectations for work and accomplishment, as set forth by my well-established inner master. The weight of these expectations kept me from enthusiastically getting on board with my training program, nor was I letting myself in on that secret part of me – my beatnik self – that did not want to be trained. I wanted to do as I had been doing, go off on my own toot, and covertly I did just that.

In some subtle way that escaped notice (or, so I assumed), I participated in graduate school at a declination, a course that angled off from those of my professors and my fellow students. As if attempting to get me on the straight-ahead track, I was relentlessly nagged at from within. The forces lined up behind my nag were mighty, they were relentless, they never slept, and they played the largest part in making academic work a tedious burden. Their greater purpose was to crush any small breath of the spirit of my beatnik self.

The struggle was dispiriting and exhausting. As I experienced it, the nagging was fully justified. If I were to survive, I believed, I had no choice but to do as I had done on that long-ago canoe trip – shoulder my burden and trudge on. Like any prisoner, I dreamed of the day I would be free and could do as I wished.

I had no affection for the character in myself I now fondly refer to as the "Beatnik," so it never occurred to me that his mixture of emotions, attitudes, and motivations might hold the better part of myself. In daily life, I felt totally antithetical to myself in anything hinting at this realm. But oddly enough, I constantly observed that this side of myself was indulged regularly throughout the day in all kinds of ways, while my serious, studious self slacked off. This was not a productive compromise.

Surprisingly, despite being treated with contempt, punished, and given free rein only on rare occasions, which I always had cause to regret, my beatnik self had the last say. The one part of me had strong ideas about what I should do and be academically and professionally, but the beatnik principle gave form to what that actually turned out to be. This was true for my dissertation research and for the work I ultimately ended up doing.

Myself as beatnik brings a different point of view to my nonmarriages. They may have been "nonmarriages" from a conventional point of view, but in my heart of hearts, they were joyful adventures in freedom, sex, and love. That acknowledgment warms my heart. "Nonmarriage" was my natural, unquestioned way of being. I resisted every push or pull toward the conventional framework of family and marriage. They were threats, and I fled from them.

I wanted to connect with the world around me – in love, work, and learning. I wanted to be alive and know who I was. But my inner being interfered with my ability to channel those energies and wishes within my culture and society in ways that were exciting and free. The social expectations I internalized had transmuted into boulders I kept pushing against.

One night when I was living in New York, I took a bus to an arcade in New Jersey. Why? Loneliness, wanderlust, desire, seeking. I have pictures I took of myself in one of the little photography booths that were everywhere at that time (this was before selfies).

"Who am I?" I wondered, as I looked at the pictures, "someone who will never find his way in the world or someone who will live a creative, fulfilling life?"

I did not know.

CHAPTER 14

Messages from the Living

Esalen

The summer I received my doctoral degree, I spent a week at the Esalen Institute in Big Sur, California. The week there turned out to be life changing.

I enrolled in a weekend yoga workshop and a five-day workshop on "sensory awareness." The yoga instructor was a young fellow who, like me, had started out studying philosophy. He had turned to yoga for health and emotional healing. He taught a way of looking at experience that I put to immediate use in managing my difficult emotional life.

Trying to stretch and fold myself into yoga positions, I made the droll discovery that I was not sure of what went where. I practiced yoga twice a day for several years. It brought me back to my body, I felt healthier, and I had a better feeling in myself.

"Sensory awareness" is an intensive guided meditation that has no explicit psychological or spiritual content. Over the course of five days, for five or six hours a day, it gently but insistently brought me into intimate contact with myself and whatever was happening in my body, breathing, and emotions.

I took a massage on my final day. I lay naked on a massage table by the hot sulfur springs that emerge from a steep hill where land meets ocean. The waters fill large concrete tubs; massage tables are arrayed in front of them. With the aroma of the water, the murmuring of springs and ocean, and the infinite vista, it is a soothing, meditative setting.

With skilled hands, my masseuse found the touch and rhythm that suited me. After a while I found myself crying deeply, an all-encompassing mourning. As I quieted down, I entered a blissful, altered state of consciousness. Gradually, as if awakening, I became aware of a low vibratory sound surrounding me or hovering over me and reaching into my heart and body, like a healing aura. I realized she was chanting "om" over me.

She left, and I slowly came back to my normal consciousness. I climbed down to the rocky shore. Everything looked alive – the moving waves, the seaweed, even the rocks. Messages from the living reached my senses and soul from everywhere. A peaceful glow filled my body, a healing balm. I needed no further evidence of the ultimate value of this state of awareness, peace, and connection with the living.

In that week, in a beautiful, peaceful setting, experiencing somatic practices exercised with skill and heart brought me closer to my deeper self and to the core of the healing process. I wanted to find a way to allow for this inner contact with myself in my daily life.

My Creek

Many years before that enchantment at the edge of the ocean, I had had a remarkably similar experience. It occurred under vastly different circumstances, but on this occasion too, I had responded to the living natural world.

I was thirteen or fourteen, and I had been home from school for a week, quite ill from the flu. In confused feverish dreams, I repeatedly struggled to make order with shifting shapes. As with other times when I had been ill, I spent the days alone in bed in my own room. I have no memory of my mother or father paying much attention to me, besides bringing me meals on trays.

Finally, I felt better. I got dressed and walked "down to the crick," a matter of crossing our yard and the neighbor's. I stood at the top of a slope that gently descends a hundred feet to the Eighteen Mile Creek. I loved the creek, the cliffs it cuts through, and the surrounding woods. It was a warm, sunny day in early spring in western New York State. Everything was fresh and moist from recently melted snow. I basked in the scene – sun, freshness, the creek flowing, a cardinal calling. As I stood there, a feeling of joy and a melding with the beauty of this beloved place filled my chest and pervaded my perception of the scene.

The Living, Healing, and Love

I did not think in these terms at the time, but now I will say that my experience on the massage table was affected by the energy of love. I do not mean that I loved my masseuse or that she loved me. I am referring to an energetic process that is the basis for that personal domain.

Her breathing aligned her emotions, and an energetic connection flowed between her hands and her heart. She was connected through her belly, her pelvis, and her genitals, through her legs to her feet and the ground. She responded to the pulsations of the ocean, air, and my body. Her "om" emerged from her inner being, and its vibration entered me and resonated with and enhanced my life pulsation.

My days leading up to the massage had been filled with giving in to body practices. They had been gentle, self-respecting, and affirming. My body was in a state in which I was ready to respond to her hands-on work. I surrendered to my deep sorrow, and relieved, responded to a flow of energy that left me in a state of bliss. This is the energy of love; it fosters change and positive development.

My teenage experience at the creek and the much later experience on the massage table by the ocean are energetically equivalent. What I experienced at the creek was also an effect of the energy of love, which fortuitously came at a time when I was healing from an illness. That day at that moment, I was happy to be alive and healthy again, and my heart opened with my love for this place on the earth. My opening allowed the beauty and aliveness around me to enter my eyes, my heart, and all my senses. And just as with the "om" during the massage, my pulsatory aliveness was enhanced.

I take a message from these experiences. Here is the living. You are experiencing the essence of being alive and conscious. Take these moments as guides and standards. This is your blessing from the living. Here is the opening to love.

This message is as vital to me now as it was those many years ago.

CHAPTER 15

An Unbidden Life

Night Hawk

By the time I arrived at Harvard, I was more used to being in my own skin. I was not so moony, and I was not so frightened of craziness or sexual aberration residing in me. I was managing in a reasonable, good-enough fashion, and I had prospects of entering a profession and making a living in an interesting, useful way. And, what mattered even more to me, being in relationships with women had become a regular part of my life.

Still, I was not on firm ground. I was starting in a new field with different language, history, and methods from what I had previously studied. Just entering academia again made me uneasy. I had no friends or acquaintances in this new milieu, so there was little to protect me from the periodic waves of lonely restlessness, agitated desires, and frustration that washed through me. Finding release infrequently in masturbation was one factor driving my frustration.

On occasional nights it all got the best of me. With no specific aim in mind, driven by restlessness and unfocused desire, I would go into Boston and wander all over the city, just as I had done in New York. I stopped in bars, and I checked out where the sex workers could be found. Once, I purchased a woman's services, as I had done occasionally in New York, but it was not a pleasant experience. It was the last time I tried to take care of myself in that way.

One morning at dawn, I found myself waiting for a bus to Harvard Square and looking at the regular folks going to work. They were a mirror showing me how out of joint I was at that moment. I arrived home wasted, and after a few hours restless sleep, I had to tolerate my fatigue and find some way of putting the day to good use. Unplanned, those nights were a combination of anguished frustration and wild urgency.

Eros Emerging

During my wanderings, I noticed a place that offered "steam baths" and announced, "Open 24/7." It was near the theater district, in a shabby, run-down corner of the city. I guessed it was a place for homosexual encounters. I was curious, but a violent fantasy lurked in the shadows of my mind. It could be an underworld hangout.

The place stimulated an unexpected, diffuse, erotic feeling. I had been aware of this place for a few years before one night, after some drinks, I got up the courage to climb a long, narrow flight of outside stairs, enter the seedy building, and sign in for a room. I did not know what I would find, but what I did find did not surprise me.

The atmosphere was unexpectedly pleasant. There were small rooms, a larger dorm-like area that was open, and downstairs there was a nice swimming pool as well as a steam room. The lighting was dim, the atmosphere quiet, and I did not feel threatened. The men were there for sexual encounters, but I did not observe any.

I visited that place a few times, and I also visited two other newer bath houses in the area, as such places became more part of the scene. Every visit was associated with a flood of unfocused erotic longing, usually coming during a period of heightened sexual frustration and distress.

My forays into the hidden nighttime homoerotic world did not end with sexual acts. I enjoyed the erotic atmosphere, and I enjoyed the erotic feeling in my own body. I was not sure what it meant and what it told me about who I was and what I wanted. At the time, the obvious escaped me. What I wanted was what I experienced: a place where I felt safe enough to feel and enjoy that erotic feeling in my body. That state was diffuse and vague, like a child's erotic feelings before sexual maturation brings focus. It nourished vague fantasies, but they did not lead to action.

No Outlet

These occasional evenings were always preceded by surging waves of erotic feeling and an agitated frustration. These feelings diffused through my tissues, but they did not find a focus or outlet in sexual acts. My nocturnal visitations were a confused search to find release. They often followed a disappointing encounter with a woman or a long period of deprivation, like a defiant self-reassurance that gave me the illusion of having resources and possibilities. "I don't need you. I can manage." But I was running away from loneliness, anguish, and suffering.

The erotic state I experienced on those nights did not develop into a homoerotic orientation. It remained what it was, an unfocused erotic state. Many years later, as a bioenergetic therapist, I learned that children involved in a sexually arousing situation with an adult or older sibling would be left with a kind of charged excitation in their body that did not have an outlet. As the child matures, the charge and excitation remain, and there is a tension that seeks discharge. But (in many cases, like mine) the excitation and tension remain separate, not becoming a part of the individual's overall sexual maturation. As a result, it is not an excitation that has a discharge. My diffuse erotic body state had just these qualities. I had no release for it, so it fueled the restlessness and frustration that sent me off on my night hawk flights. It interfered with my capacity to learn and work. I have little reason to question that its origins, in part, were in my relationship with my brother. My relationship with my mother may have provided a background level of excitation.

Sonny, Again

One evening, maybe two years into my graduate program, I was with Esther, a woman I met one weekend at a resort in Maine. She met me at the department offices, and we were about to leave to go back to my apartment. I stopped to chat with Ron, a fellow graduate student. As we chatted, I became aware that, at that moment, my feeling of ease, familiarity, and wish for friendship with Ron pulled at me more strongly than my wish to go back to my apartment with Esther, which then felt a little bleak.

This was my first conscious awareness of what I came to name a "homoerotic life." After this I was aware of similar feelings on other occasions. From that first time, I recognized that I was missing my brother. He was still alive at the time, but we had no contact with each other.

He died in 1965 age forty-one; I was thirty-one. We had never talked about our early relationship, but two curious events involving his wife, Sally, are suggestive.

I was visiting, and the three of us were together in their car.

Sally, in a stage voice says, "Bert, what is fellatio?"

I suppress myself to keep from saying, "It's a blow job," and waited to see what was up.

My brother, in an anxious, academic, medical voice, says, "It involves sexual gratification by the mucous membranes of the mouth."

I thought to myself, "Odd. A charade."

Sally's seemingly out of the blue question felt rehearsed. Nothing more was said.

One evening during the last days of his life, I drove Sally to their home in Niagara Falls. As we were talking, she came out with something to the effect, "Here we are, the man we both love is dying." I was a bit startled. In the context of the same conversation, Sally said, "And it was not good for either of you," referring to the relationship between me and my brother. Her comments suggested conversations with my brother about our relationship or perhaps her own observations of the two of us.

So, for him, there seems to have been an uneasy aura around our connection, something I had not been aware of. At one point during a remission, he came to Boston for a consultation. I met him at the airport. I have a distinct and painful image of our meeting. I found him walking down a sidewalk towards me. As I started to greet him openly with excitement, I saw him wince and pull himself in, as if to ward me off. Of course, he was dealing with a terminal illness, but his retraction seemed to be a reaction to my excitement about seeing him and my love. During the time he was in Boston, we did not talk, and he spent most of his time with a friend.

So It Was

My beguiling erotic feeling originated in the stimulation of childhood intimacies. My sexual development as a boy had been diverted and partially shut down by the impact of my experience with my brother, the person in my family I loved the most. I entered another transition point in my mid-twenties, and my quest for fulfillment in this new context opened new possibilities for sexual development. This quest brought along with it awareness of emotions that had been stopped in my childhood. I recognized some of those emotions as missing my brother. But I did not experience the connections of my more erotic sensations with my childhood. Until I had the time to learn about them and explore them, they felt "unbidden," as if they were not quite mine.

All these experiences were reliving earlier experiences. Becoming aware of them and identifying them allowed me to resolve and let go of unbidden experiences. That left me freer to love and be sexual with the person now sharing my life.

At the time of my brother's nocturnal surprise visitation, when I was a boy, he was a frightened, still adolescent airman, preparing for war. He was too young to have had much, if any, experience of sexual love with a woman. Under those circumstances and getting free of a military air base for a furlough, it is not inconceivable that he succumbed to finding comfort and relieving tension in some manner with the convenient presence of an adoring little brother. Even with no physical contact, as a boy, I could have been affected by his sexual feelings and private masturbations.

CHAPTER 16

Newfoundland

A Sanctuary

The house I had bought when Kaelin and I were together was in a small town called Pepperell, about forty miles northwest of Cambridge, Massachusetts, where I had an office. Kaelin and I moved in there in 1975, and I continued to live there after she moved out in 1980. I was living there with my two dogs when Vellie and I got together. During our first few years together, we split our time between Vellie's Watertown condo and my house in Pepperell.

We were becoming more at home with each other. To manage her energies, Vellie cut down on her work hours. This new arrangement set the stage for some memorable evenings. Vellie would leave her office early, and when I arrived at her condo, she would be there, with a nice meal ready, and sometimes wearing a sexy, clinging green gown.

The decision that Vellie would move in with me and make Pepperell her home was a big step for each of us. Despite some displays of ambivalence on my part, by the time she crossed the threshold, I was happy we were living together.

We both loved the place. Woods surrounded the house, the air was fresh, and we had an organic garden. Winter snow was followed by banks of mountain laurel blossoms in the spring, and in the fall a remarkable maple tree in front of the house turned brilliant red and orange. We had a small squad of pets: my two Rhodesian Ridgebacks, Vellie's little Lasso Apso, and her cat.

The house was our retreat, a safe place for healing. We had rooms where we could each go for bioenergetic work or to withdraw. We did not have to worry about making noise in our country seclusion. It was a beautiful setting for the occasions on which we used LSD or MDMA.

Our retreat was also the scene of repeated episodes in which our inner disturbances were ignited. These were doubly devastating because we dearly desired to be together in love and sexual intimacy. Very often we were. But we felt heartbroken every time we cycled through one of these painful storms.

We were still in the grips of reliving childhood disturbance, trauma, loss of connection, and aloneness. Love had not neutralized their negative effects. We realized we did not know or understand the experience of loving and being loved.

A Vacation Gone Awry

One summer we teetered at the edge of losing each other.

We made plans to fly to Newfoundland and do some car camping. I bought a large tent for us, and I looked forward to our being together in it. The first evening, as I put up the tent, and more so once we got inside, I was flooded with erotic desire. Besides arranging our sleeping bags that is my only memory of our being in the tent together.

The next morning, after we had breakfast and began driving, Vellie told me that she felt sleepy and was going to curl up on the seat and nap. At this, I went crazy and began yelling at her in a horrible way. I could not or would not stop.

That night we stayed at a small hotel, and it was her turn to yell at me and tell me she could not stand it anymore and was going to leave me. I became quiet, feeling deeply hurt. The next day my efforts to make peace failed. That night Vellie insisted on having her own room and shut me out. The vacation ended, and we returned home, both believing our relationship was ending.

Back home, I was convinced that my eruption in Newfoundland had been set off by Vellie's coldness and rejection of my excitement about making love with her that evening in the tent. On top of this, without saying any more about it, she was planning to leave. I sank into despair and grief that felt like dying. I retreated to my study and cried daily for three weeks. Vellie was unmoved.

One day I went upstairs from my study, found Vellie in the kitchen, and said, "But don't you see, we're saying goodbye to all of this – our home here, our garden, everything."

At this, Vellie broke down in tears. She lay down on the wooden floor in the kitchen, petting it and saying goodbye to it – beautiful pine wood flooring. She was saying goodbye to the many beautiful things in our life.

Grieving for those weeks shifted my conviction that Vellie was the cause of my despair. My feelings softened, we both found our hearts again, and we were able to reconnect.

What Happened?

Vellie always said she could not understand what had happened that morning in Newfie. I saw this as her lack due to some peculiar blind spot. But she was perfectly clear about one thing: Whatever had happened, she would no longer tolerate my raging at her. She got through to me, and I began to change.

Still, in my mind, I had no doubt about what had happened. Vellie saying she was going to curl up and take a nap, threw a switch in my brain that shot my emotions to a cataclysmic level. I "knew" that the night before she had not responded to my excitement and my erotic state. She had disappointed me horribly and betrayed me. I was thrown into a state of rage, which I "knew" was a direct result of Vellie's emotional and sexual absence. Saying she was going to curl up and nap felt like an abandonment, and that feeling brought me back to what I then believed was her rejection from the night before.

Later that day when Vellie confronted me, I entrenched as a double victim: disappointed and betrayed and then blamed and punished for my "natural," "understandable," and "justified" reaction.

A Startling Revelation

Moving on, we acknowledged this event as one of our darkest moments, but afterwards, neither of us ever took it as a basis for recriminations. From time to time, when I thought of it, I felt a dark shadow and a tinge of feeling that I had been wrongly injured, and the hurt was never set right.

In subsequent years, we rarely referenced what had been a wrenching experience for both of us. Writing about it for my report led to a mutually sympathetic discussion.

Vellie told me again that there was something about the whole uproar she had never understood. She told me that the next morning I had seemed perfectly happy packing up the tent and getting ready to move on.

Once again, I described what I remembered as having been my experience from the evening before: an intense erotic state and disappointment. Vellie realized – for the first time – I was telling her we had not made love that night in the tent.

She said, "But we did make love that night. We did. We made love that night."

I was dumbfounded and appalled.

I believed her without question. At some point that morning, my experience of our lovemaking from just the evening before became lost to me. Its place was taken by the conviction that Vellie had disappointed me in the worst way.

At the time, she had no idea of what was going on with me. My capacity to talk about myself was still limited. I had learned early on to keep my feelings secret, especially sexual feelings.

My gratitude that we stayed together is beyond words.

CHAPTER 17

An Erotic Haze

A Summer Day

One beautiful summer day in Pepperell, we decided we would benefit from an experience with MDMA.

As we planned the session, I experienced a wave of familiar, diffuse, erotic feelings and longings. This same erotic state emerged in anticipation of every MDMA experience. I wanted it to carry over into the experience and find expression with Vellie, but we found that under the influence of MDMA, we did not have intercourse. But we were always naked, and I enjoyed a sensual pleasure in my own body.

We planned to be by ourselves for the first two hours, then get together and see what evolved. At the appointed time, Vellie went to the sunny, open space in the house where we were to meet. She could see me outside.

Later, she told me, "You were sitting on a log in the sun, sweating."

She could see I was absorbed in my own world, so she did not call me. Eventually, she came outside and gently approached me. She saw I was still off in my own world.

She asked me, "Are you with your brother?"

I told her, "Yes, I am."

She asked me, "Has he been sexual with you?"

I did not have an answer. Vellie told me later my eyes "glazed over," and I drifted off. Vellie left me with myself.

For years after, I could recall the sensual sensations of sitting on that log in front of our garden, sweating in the hot sun. I was wrapped in an erotic haze that did not come to focus in my genitals, and I felt content. I was not aware of specific memories or fantasies, but in my feeling, I was with my brother.

At some point I decided to go back into the house.

The next thing I remember is Vellie saying, "I think your brother sexually abused you." We had been talking about this issue in the context of both of our lives for some time. We came to understand that an adult's sexuality could impact a developing child in any number of ways besides direct physical contact.

I was surprised, taken off guard, and – in a strange way – pleased. That meant that at one time I really did have a special relationship with him. That was my feeling and those were my thoughts when I heard what Vellie said. The erotic haze remained in my body as a residue from the period when my brother was the one I loved.

A Useful Child

Beginning in my late twenties, I experienced that erotic haze – not every day – but a number of times. It remained part of an underground inner world. As I got to know myself, I learned about other indelible imprints left on my sexual development from childhood. Some of these were the upshot of being the child who conveniently served as a kind of family psychological trash can. Into me were dropped various unowned negative identities, impulses, images, and traits that circulated in the histories and inner worlds of my parents and siblings. They stimulated worries about myself.

In my family, as a boy, I gathered that sex was something dark, secret, and potentially dangerous. A distrust of my sexuality grew in me, later leading me to be apprehensive about what bad things might result from masturbating or sexual intercourse. For a while "homosexuality" – which I knew nothing about – was one of my apprehensions.

Lester

One troubling, unspoken family matter that tangled in my sexual development and identity had to do with my mother's brother, Lester. He lived most of his adult life in a state psychiatric hospital, warehoused as chronically mentally ill. His story is deeply poignant to me. It seems he had no one in his life who cared about him, and he was simply abandoned.

Mother saw her brother in me and compared me to him. "Lester read a lot," she would say, or "Lester would go in the corner and make noises" (something I did not do). His condition was not talked about, which left me with a spooky anxiety about "craziness," something scary that resulted in ostracism and abandonment. As a child, I did not think I was crazy, but I did not know for sure, and I could not tell what I would be as time went on.

A few years after I began graduate school, I drove from Cambridge to Pilgrim State Hospital on Long Island to visit Lester, this shadow from my past. Immediately after I introduced myself, he responded, "You're Bert Helfaer's son." He had seen no one in our family for decades.

I was struck that he acknowledged me not as his sister's son, but as his brother-in-law's. Sadly, I did not keep up contact with him, and I heard that he died a few years later. This man mattered to me because my mother identified me with him. I saw his sad fate.

Jew

My parents were secular, assimilated Jews. Nothing in our home or our way of life so much as hinted at Judaism. But in the idiosyncratic convolutions of our family psychology, another hidden trait that I ended up holding was being the Jew. As the child of Jews, I held the consciousness of the dirty Jew, the kike of their family memories. After they married, my brother and sister established Jewish culture in their homes by affiliating with a temple and joining a Jewish community. I never followed this path.

I witnessed anti-Semitism as a nine- or ten-year-old boy one summer at a YMCA camp near Buffalo – "C" as in Christian and Buffalo as in a city with many Polish families. Fortunately, I was practiced at being invisible in terms of Jewishness.

I was the only Jewish boy in all the years I was in school in my town. No one ever even mentioned it, but by the time I was in high school, I took it for granted that being Jewish was something to be ashamed of. There was one Jewish girl in my high school class. I was able to acknowledge her presence, and we went to a school dance together one year. In my mind, I would try to understand how it was that I was Jewish. What did it mean, and why did I have to be that?

A few years ago, I participated in a residential workshop where we did a lengthy exercise about our shame; my shame was named, "dirty, masturbating little Jew."

My father did not engage with his heritage. A hateful rage emerged from him from time to time focusing on racial matters, black people, Polish people, once or twice on my sister's Jewish husband, as if, as far as I could know, he wanted nothing much to do with us – us Jews.

My mother's attitudes were similar, but for different reasons. Her father was a rabbi, and she hated her father. She said her father had abandoned her and her mother, a mother who was left saying, "Ich bin ganz allein" (I am all alone). She had other disparaging things to say about him too.

An editorial page cartoon from a local Pennsylvania newspaper, dated 1910, features my grandfather, Joseph Leiser. It shows the rabbi, dressed simply in jacket and tie, in his study surrounded by books and papers and showing titles of the books he had written, a novel and *A History of American Judaism*. The caption is, "Something Great Yet. Just Wait." He received recognition in the Jewish community as well as in the broader community. He was the only person in the extended family whose life I wanted mine to mirror, even in part. As a child, here was another way in which I fell into the wrong camp.

Jerking Off and Other Outrages

I learned about masturbation from my friend, Larry. We were in ninth grade. He told me how it was done.

"It works. Ask Connell," he said, as if he needed backup from another pal for the veracity of his information. "Then you feel guilty," he said.

I asked him, "Guilty?" He just said, "Yeah."

That night I tried it. Then in a little while, I tried it again. It did work, and I liked it, and I enjoyed it many nights for the rest of my high school years, and beyond.

In high school I went through agony the first time I called a girl for a date. It took days. I got a horrible gut feeling when I started to pick up the phone. I was not aware of all the shameful connections with masturbation that had crept into my mind, including Lester's sad fate.

On My Own

My launch into adolescent sexuality marked a divide in my relationship with my father. Before, that is before I was an adolescent masturbator, I have fond memories of occasional times of warm companionship. The period after was characterized by an uneasy distance. Over the years, I greatly missed having a connection with my father. Later, I felt I abandoned him, as he had abandoned me.

If any overt sexual activity had happened between myself and my brother, or if I had been subject to abuse in other ways, would my parents have been aware of it? Possibly, but it would not have been something they would deal with. My parents were both dedicated to keeping a quiet milieu so as not to upset or disturb Mother in any way. I learned this clearly on the one and only occasion that I know of when my father did do something that disturbed her.

One night, before my teen years, he attended a dinner for the management of the company he worked for. He came (or rather was brought) home in a seriously intoxicated state. He may have passed out at the dinner. Except for an occasional cocktail with company, he never drank, at home or anywhere else. This event was totally uncharacteristic. I watched as he undressed for bed looking shaky, humiliated, and unwell. I was scared and worried for him.

I thought my mother would take care of him, so I was surprised and a bit stunned when she said, "And just when I was starting to feel better."

She took his distress as an injury to herself, a threat – not to his well-being and his reputation at work, but to her own well-being.

She might have felt the same way on the occasion when I was overwhelmed with grief at my brother's departure and return to the air force. My crying and wish to be excused from school would have been an imposition, a threat to her mental equilibrium. Perhaps she took it as additional evidence of my potential for being another Lester. After that, and by the time I was twelve or thirteen, I felt that my life was a private matter and that I was on my own.

Assignment

My parents were not punitive or judgmental toward me, and I came and went as I wished; but I had little warm contact or communication with them from early on. They seemed to accept me as I was, but at the same time, they both seemed to see me in a dubious light, as if to say, "How is this boy going to turn out?" As the youngest child, alone in myself and with them, I was sensitive to their inner worlds. In this milieu, I took into myself the rejected images, feelings, and impulses that I picked up from their cues, as I have described. Along with these, the love relationship with my brother fomented the erotic fixation I described. In these and other ways, diverse, anomalous threads wove into my sexuality, giving rise to disturbing complexities in my feelings about myself as a man and the way I experienced desire and sex. Because of this, as the years of my early adulthood went on, I eventually realized that I needed to find my way to being a man who has the capacity for love. I took this as my assignment.

CHAPTER 18

Of Prostates and Masturbation

Masturbation represents the executive agency of the whole
of infantile sexuality and is, therefore, able to take over
the sense of guilt attaching to it.

– Sigmund Freud, *Three Essays on the
Theory of Sexuality* (1966)

Bad News

We returned to our home in Pepperell in the spring of
2002 after a two-year stay in Israel. In June I learned
I had prostate cancer. I was in tears, both with grief
and feeling I was letting Vellie down. I was not worried about
dying. Already traumatized sexually, I worried about loss of
sexual function. Four months later, small bits of silver wire,
loaded with a radioactive element, were implanted into my
prostate through my perineum. Vellie made a doughnut-shaped
pad for me to sit on; otherwise, sitting was unbearable.

The cancer diagnosis shocked me. Vellie and I were doing

our best to cope with our serious personal distress. Now there was a second source of stress. Combining them exacerbated the effects of both, and I entered a period of several years when I was living in or on the edge of a state of posttraumatic disorder. Long before this news, I told myself that if I was ever confronted with a serious illness, I would drop as much work as possible and devote my energy to getting well. Our practices in Massachusetts were already on hold, so free of work responsibilities, my days could center around healing work and doing as I wished.

A New Kind of Seminar

I attributed my cancer to disturbed sexual development and functioning that affected my pelvis and genital organs. To me, this meant my healing work had to reach into my body to the very tissues that were affected.

There was no question in my mind that regular masturbation is essential to maintain prostate health and health in general. I had an on and off history of prostatitis, sometimes resulting in painful contractions. I had not masturbated often or regularly enough, and I was painfully aware of my years of sexual frustration and a chronically tense body state that was distracting and preoccupying.

What I needed to do in this situation was obvious to me. I inaugurated what I humorously (I thought) called my "masturbation seminar." It was held once a week, on a set night. The "curricula" of the seminar is to masturbate consciously (mindfully) with the intention, not merely for release, but of paying attention to all emerging experience: anxiety, shame, body states, and any other reactions, thoughts, and fantasies.

The seminar turned out to be a challenge. It was summer when I began. We had an open porch, very private, overlooking our garden and woods. I set up a lawn chair and began my seminar there, naked in the sun. Vellie was entirely supportive and encouraging. Nonetheless, my anxious self-consciousness quickly drove me to retreat to my study on the lower level of the house, where I could close the door and let down the blind – as if I were frightened of being caught. Well, I was.

From the outset, the seminar did just what it was supposed to do. Stimulating the tissues of my pelvis and genital organs evoked anxiety, self-consciousness, shame, inhibition, and other miserable feelings, thoughts, and fantasies. This recurred week after week. I understood these disturbing experiences as post-traumatic symptoms resulting from violations to my developing sexuality experienced during childhood and adolescence. In those first weeks, months, and for a few years, there were many evenings when I simply could not generate any genital feeling, or if I did, it was not sufficient to bring me to an orgasm. Eventually I would end the session, go to bed, and gain the comfort of Vellie's warm, sleeping presence.

Another Frontier

My seminar stimulated an internet search, which led me to the spiritually oriented growth work of Joseph Kramer. Here I met another frontier. His program is in the same spirit as mine. Masturbation, done deliberately, with awareness, can be a practice for relieving the effects of sexual trauma and shame, for expanding the capacity for erotic pleasure, and for facilitating the development of the capacity for love. Kramer and other sexological activists understood that erotic pleasure is a healing force, and the capacity for it is necessary for health. They developed erotic practices suited to these ends.

Kramer developed what he called "Taoist erotic massage." Watching a CD of the massage, I was moved to see the one receiving the massage reach a nearly ecstatic state. It looked to me like an advanced form of my masturbation seminar. Workshops based on Kramer's work were offered by an organization he and others had established, called the Body Electric School. Their introductory weekend for men is called "Celebrating the Body Erotic," and again, it looked a lot like my masturbation seminar writ large. I was excited about it, and I thought it had the potential for being helpful. I decided to give it a go.

This first weekend was not easy. It was a couple of months before my cancer treatment, and I went to it with that hanging over my head. I reached no erotic heights. But being with a large group of men who were just as focused on their genital experience as I was went a long way to "decriminalizing" masturbation and allowing it to become an ordinary part of a sexual life. My masturbation seminar was validated.

Subsequently, I participated in three weeklong residential workshops and one more weekend workshop. My posttraumatic symptoms were active in all of them. I was anxious, and I often moved into terror and dissociation, or on a few occasions, rage. My capacity for experiencing erotic feelings was limited, and I felt sexually damaged.

At the last Body Electric weekend I took part in, I found resolution for an issue at the heart of my sexual disturbance. One of the teachers was a rabbi, and the workshop was meant to combine erotic practice and Jewish celebration – a powerful combination. I went, but I did not know if I would be able to participate without being overly frightened, dissociating, or going into a rage.

During the first day of the workshop, I discovered that I could not. Naked, we explored touching and being touched genitally. I became frightened, overwhelmed, and I could not manage the exercise. The next morning, as we all stood naked in a circle the trainer gave me the opportunity to talk about my decision to leave.

I began talking by saying, "My brothers," and immediately commenced crying while telling the group about my dissociation.

Soon I was crying fully and deeply. I had not expected such intense emotion, and I did not know what I was crying about. I suspected that my sorrow had to do with separation from my brother. But Vellie saw it more deeply. My grief was about relinquishing once and for all the erotic connection I had felt or imagined with him and the fantasy of realizing it in my life. I left my "erotic brothers" for good.

A Somatic-Energetic Healing Practice

At the same time that I instigated my masturbation seminar, I began daily bioenergetic sessions in which I focused on my body. I used breathing and somatic techniques to facilitate softening and release of chronic tensions associated with a posttraumatic condition. Many of these tensions are held in muscles, but they are complex structures – armor – which are engaged with the autonomic nervous and the vagal nervous systems. As armor softens, it releases energy, affects (body states), and emotions that are related to the original traumatizing experiences. This process can be painful and frightening, and it can be exhilarating.

I started my sessions with breathing exercises and energizing my body. I lay on a bed and kicked, and I lay stretched back over a rolled-up blanket placed either on the bed or strapped to a stool. The musculature of the breathing apparatus is stretched and energized this way and breathing deepens.

Then I would work with tensions in my jaw by biting on a

towel, growling, baring my teeth and thrusting my jaw forward. I pressed my knuckles into the tight muscles at the corner of the jaw. This was painful, but effective. It often led to crying.

Commonly, there is a ring of chronic tension (armor) around the head. It includes the top of the head, encircles the whole skull at the level of the eyes, and includes the occipital region at the back of the head. I worked with these ocular tensions every day, and it had a strong effect. My eyes would "go off." They went out of focus, and I saw double. I felt stunned and dizzy, as if I had been hit, or as if something had shocked me. I gave in to these sensations, allowing my head to move with the feelings and allowing sounds to go with it. If I were standing, I let myself fall on the bed and there continue with movement and sound. I experienced states of shock, confusion, and feelings of going "crazy," along with states of denial and disbelief.

Each segment of the body has its own armor: the ocular segment, as I just described; the neck and throat; the chest; the diaphragm; the abdomen; and finally, the pelvis, including the legs. Each segment gets attention in my sessions, according to the way the session flows. My work with the segmental armor softened tensions and allowed freer access to emotional expression – the grief, fear, terror, anger, and rage associated with my childhood.

As the last part of a somatic-energetic session I used exercises that brought feeling and energy to the chronic tensions in my pelvis and to the site of the cancer. At this point my somatic-energetic session converged with the function of the masturbation seminar.

The contact with my somatic self in the sessions was comforting and healing. Looking back, I see these sessions as crucial for my healing and development. They facilitated a steady, strong movement of energy and feeling that reached into the tissues involved in my underlying developmental disturbances, so they were essential to affecting change.

Our home in Pepperell was quiet and safe. I was grateful for the opportunity to be there with Vellie and be free to pursue my healing practices.

Aliyah

In March 2003, we went together to teach our final workshop in Norway. When we returned home, I continued my healing work, and we made our arrangements for Aliyah. By early fall we were in Israel.

CHAPTER 19

Demons in the Orchard

But these troubles are past, and thou wilt read these
records of a period so dolorous to us both as the legend
of some hideous dream that can return no more.

– Thomas de Quincey, *The Confessions of an
English Opium Eater* ([1856] 1983)

Hapardess

We lived in Israel from 2000 to 2012, with brief trips to
the States two or three times a year. In 2006 we sold
our house in Pepperell and purchased an apartment
in Kfar Saba, a large town north of Tel Aviv. It was a two-floor
"penthouse" of an older, six-floor building. A broad balcony on
three sides gave outside space and views south, west, and north.
Large windows and sliding doors brought in an abundance of
light and air, making living there a pleasure. Tel Aviv decorated
the skyline twenty kilometers to the south.

We had offices in two rooms upstairs, and the living room held our small training groups. Our neighborhood benefited from proximity to large agricultural fields of organic strawberries, grown January through May. Hapardess (the orchard in Hebrew) Street was itself merely a pedestrian lane connecting two streets. This was our setting for six years.

A Time of Trial

The move to Hapardess marked the beginning of our time of crisis and trial. My battles raged on and off – with my demons, within myself, and between me and Vellie – for six years. In survival mode, I burned off stress hormones at the gym and on long walks. My best friend told me I looked tortured when I met him in the States on one of our trips back. I was not aware of that, but I knew I felt like hell – a burning lake of pain filled me.

My thought was, "If I am ever going to find, or create, a life of peace, happiness, and love, it has to emerge out of the life I am living now." I just did not know if Vellie or I would break before that happened. In my heart, I believed myself to be capable of warmth and intimacy, but between us lay the long-held tensions of traumatic experience conditioned into our bodies and nervous systems.

This was the breeding ground of my demons, and I jigged to their tunes throughout our sojourn on Hapardess. Regular outbursts of conflict, disaffection, and alienation ended in paroxysms of crying – sobbing, really – always from a broken heart, and often from the edge of despair. Each such occasion renewed my dread that, for me, there would be no love, not with Vellie, and not with anyone else, and this made my grief even more heart wrenching. At times, my faith in us as a couple wore to shreds.

Crossing Boundaries

Two distinct events broke the invisible boundaries that had been containing us and constraining our demons. On both occasions, I crossed Vellie's boundaries.

1. A Bad Word

We were in the States, staying in Vellie's condo, completing our preparations to return to Israel and move into our apartment. It was evening, and I had just returned from teaching a satisfying two-day workshop. I was eager to be with her for the evening and make love. Vellie was disturbed from a long phone conversation with a friend, and she kept talking anxiously, trying to resolve her feelings.

After a time, as she continued talking, I felt that she was not going to be with me, and from feeling happy and excited, I began to feel horrible. I asked her to stop and told her what was going on. She saw that I was distressed and was very sympathetic.

At this point, Vellie began to panic, as she often does when she believes she has caused me to be upset, fearing the loss of our connection, even briefly. I still felt terrible, but by then I just wanted to go to bed. I encouraged Vellie to come to bed with me and let herself calm down.

After a time, believing I was asleep, Vellie got up and went into the other room. I was not asleep. Lying alone in bed in the dark, I was overtaken with a horrible feeling of loss and disappointment. After a while I could not contain it.

I got up and barged into the other room demanding, "What is going on with you?"

She was lying on the floor with a breathing roll under her back. She replied that she was breathing and letting herself get in touch with herself. But I paid no attention.

In a rage, I burst out with, "You're being imbecilic."
She was still lying over the roll on the floor. She was shocked.
She said, "Why don't you just kill me."

I had been outraged and in pain, but now I froze. I was
horrified at what I had done, this cruel utterance. It could not
be undone. I did not even know how to apologize. My cruel
verbal attack crossed the boundary of respect and care inherent
in our relationship, and that boundary should never have been
challenged. Doing so awakened the effects of her early abusive
experiences of just this kind of treatment. I had reproduced
with horrifying accuracy how, at times, her father had treated
her: the rage, the craziness, the total disrespect, and undermining her sense of safety, leaving her feeling threatened.

In the following painful weeks, I was remorseful, and my
heart hurt for her. She looked fragile and anxious, and her
resilience was much diminished. But I did not entirely let go
of my own sense of injury.

2. Unfortunate Irritability

Both shaken, we returned to Israel in July of 2006 and set
about the task of furnishing our new apartment for our work
and daily living. During those first days, I again crossed her
boundary. We had gone to Jaffo to the shuk – the open-air
flea market – to get a secondhand table for our kitchen. Vellie
was driving on the way home. It was the first time she had
driven in Israel, and she was nervous. She said something to
me about her tension, which I did not hear. I answered her
irritably, with no empathy or understanding, because, out of
my misperception and irritability, I was judging her for creating
a bad feeling between us.

I held on to my resentment, and the next day, I did worse.
We were planning to get furniture for my office. Vellie found

enough resilience to kindly offer to go with me. She saw that I was starting to withdraw and go into isolation. I acted indifferently to her offer. I acted as if I had dropped her, almost as if she did not exist; just as, early on, I had "dropped" my mother.

At that moment, treating Vellie in this manner, as if I were erasing her presence, was another instance of crossing her boundary. I should never have treated her that way under any circumstance, and now we had just moved to Israel where she was not only an immigrant but also not Jewish. We were used to relying on each other, and I betrayed that trust.

This was the end of the line for her. And it signaled the start of the time of crisis for both of us.

Transformation

Vellie was shaken, and in her shaking, she wrought a great transformation within herself – not gradually – then and there. I learned later that she took the milestone of her recent seventieth birthday as a wake-up call. Now she told herself,

> I'm seventy years old. It's time I take charge of my own life. It's time I live by self-respect and expect and demand that I be treated with respect. I will no longer accept Phil, or anyone, yelling at me, or treating me in any way other than with total respect. I don't care if I'm right or wrong, I will no longer be yelled at. And I will have respect.

She insisted on being safe from anger, accusation (however subtle), and any kind of disrespect. She would no longer accept always being one down, and she would not accept the assumption that she was the problem, or that she needed fixing. She would no longer accept being the one at fault; the one to blame; the one to say, "I'm sorry"; the one who was responsible for my unhappiness. From then on, this was her ground, and she never wavered. Any time I so much as hinted at crossing any of those lines, she said, "No." Just, "No," and that was it.

Remarkably, Vellie took on her new way of being without making it a fight. She just did it. And she maintained it in the same way. No fighting, no ultimatums or putting me down, she just did it.

With courage, energized self-respect, and with love for herself and for me, she claimed her life for herself and stood on solid, new ground. I did not want to challenge her claims to being her own person, having her own life, and being treated at all times with respect. I knew in my heart of hearts that what she was doing was right for her, and that it was essential for what we wished for together.

Because of You ... But Maybe Me

At the heart of all my confrontations with Vellie there had always been the implicit belief that "my pain is because of her" (whichever "her" it might be at the time). This "because of" is like the color red. It is what I saw, it cannot be described. Red is red. If I hurt, it was because of her. I never spoke those words to her, but my behavior clearly conveyed my attitude, and Vellie experienced it. Within myself, unspoken, frequently repeated refrains, which I only partially acknowledged to myself, maintained and kept alive the smoldering fire of this resentment:

Again, I'm unhappy and suffering – because of her. She's impossible. But now, here I am connected to this disappointing woman who hurts me, who doesn't bother with me, and I'm left in my anger and resentment. I am all wound up with her, preoccupied, obsessed. I'll figure her out, and I'll make her understand and change! And feel contrite! Finally, someone will say, "I'm so sorry."

These ruminations were the accompaniment of knotted up, dark, turmoil and unhappiness. I keep pushing to figure out, fix, and change her. Another theme joins in. I try to push it away, but it soon infiltrates:

> I argue with myself. I feel terrible. I'm trying to talk myself out of the possibility that I have caused our pain and suffering; it's because of me.

> Is it? Maybe there is something terribly wrong and bad about me. Is there? ... And it probably has something to do with my penis, excitement, and longings. Even if I don't have words, it all lodges there eventually – right there in the whole genital, perineum, anal area.

This whirlwind went on in my mind and body up to the time Vellie acted. I protected myself by putting up a wall of confrontation and by pushing her to "understand" and straighten herself out. These energies and my cleverness were what Vellie had been up against.

Another Golden Rule

Being the "helper" was my preferred way of insinuating that our difficulty of the moment was the result of her "issues." This meant the focus stayed on Vellie. We talked about her. And I did not have to talk about myself in a way that threatened me. Unfortunately, in this way I deprived myself of the possibility of pursuing my own development.

Vellie stopped me using this strategy by laying down a simple practical rule. Her rule was an arrow aimed at the core of my modus vivendi. She would not listen to me talk about or ask about what I claimed were her problems. I could no longer offer to "help" her. She would not accept my saying anything about what I thought was going on with her. When we talked, I had to talk about my own feelings and problems.

Vellie's action pushed me to take the step I had not been able to take. At the same time, her way of being with me provided me enough safety to face my fears and pain. I began to take account of myself in a way I had not been able to do before.

The Cord Is Cut

This new golden rule had an immediate effect. I felt shaky and anxious. I was in stark confrontation with my inner emotional state in a way I had not previously been able to manage, and I did not know if I had the wherewithal to handle it. I experienced a state of aloneness that had always been unbearable for me, and I was on my own.

I had no way of avoiding my awareness that the pain and suffering I kept experiencing was not only not caused by Vellie, it actually had nothing to do with her. It was in me because it was part of me, the traumatic effects of early life experience. I had managed in all sorts of ways up to then to download the sources of those effects into my relationship with Vellie. Without those strategies, all the pain came back into me. This was the most painful and difficult part of the whole experience. It not only hurt a lot, but my whole experience of reality – who I was and who we were together – shifted.

At first, I experienced a frightening loss. Once I had some experience with being present for myself and attending to my own being, I accepted and appreciated the separation. Then my experience was not one of loss. It was self-affirming. Similarly, when I discovered I could contain my pain and anxiety, I saw it as my capacity to foster my own development and claim my own agency. "Self-respect" is an appropriate term for the whole development that took place. This active process was not new to me, but now it went deeper and was more thorough, and it brought new, exciting, and heartwarming experiences.

Demons to Dragons

Towards the end of our stay on Hapardess, the possibility of a life together in gentleness and love emerged into view. The ferocious energy of the demons was spent or diverted into more favorable channels. Our emotional life softened, and we felt tender kernels of trust. I wanted badly to believe in it, this bluebird of happiness.

Settling into Vellie's condo back in the States, we tentatively enjoyed a newfound sense of safety, peace, and love, with only occasional flickers of discord. Our bodies quieted down from the uproar. That kindly process continued, and as we built our new home together it was more and more solidly established within each of us.

In retrospect, those years seem remarkable to me. I lived the experience of my awakened traumatic past with all its fear, terror, and horror. I contained my upheaval, pain, grief, and rage. I delved the depths of that chaos and found healing, discovered my self, and found the capacity for love. I did what needed to be done, and I experienced Vellie doing so as well.

With our work, I learned to live in a new reality. My partner is not the cause of my misery. I can trust her. I can trust her goodness and her love. And more than that I can enjoy and love her without worrying something terrible will come of it. Joyful!

When the idea that I needed to learn to love first entered my mind, I had no inkling about the kind of learning that would entail. I could not anticipate it would be a lifetime odyssey. Nor did I imagine I would be meeting demons that are real enough. And maybe furthest from anything I could imagine was that the demons threatening to tear me apart could be transformed – as if into dragons – ensuring my safety and guarding the treasures of living in this new reality.

CHAPTER 20

Being Together/Being With

Looking Back in Wonder

One day, after moving into our new house in North Carolina, I idly picked a book from its shelf. Opening it, I saw a familiar inscription:

> July 3, 1986
>
> The day after we delivered the *third* Journal to N.Y. – Just 3 days after [sic] A.H.A. – We will look back on these days in wonder!
>
> Love, Vel

Reading this message, written so many years ago, filled my heart, and tears came to my eyes. I felt Vellie's soul.

On the occasion she refers to, we had loaded boxes with 1,500 copies of our institute's journal in a van and delivered them to an office in New York City. We enjoyed doing such things together and turned them into adventures. "A.H.A." refers to a recent shared MDMA experience that made this adventure more wondrous.

We do look back in wonder. Times of harmony, pleasure, and joy have always been part of our life, even in otherwise dark times.

Stalwart Love

We stayed together through the months of pain and distress on Hapardess. We stayed together following the first ominous harbinger, my explosion in the restaurant in Harvard Square. Serious consideration of separating did come up, but when I questioned myself about staying together, I immediately felt my love for Vellie and hers for me. Our life together could be emotionally painful, but it was alive and real. We were engaged in the experience and with each other, and when we lost our focus on healing and self-development, we managed to get back to it.

I held to my intention to free myself, to live the only life I had, and share it with Vellie. If she saw my intent wavering, she would say, "But, Phil, we're on this journey together," a mantra that reassured me. Staying together might mean days of suffering, but more importantly, it meant that each of our strengths was doubled, and our dedication to our development stayed vital.

I told myself that however tumultuous our situation, we were doing exactly what we needed to do. Doubts emerged, and sometimes despair, either when I felt alone or when I saw Vellie's suffering. Eventually, I could reassure myself that even these nadirs were part of a healing path.

My fate had left me as I was. I did not choose it, and I was not making it up. I took the only path to freedom I knew. I was fortunate to have personal and financial resources that allowed me to stay with my course of healing and development. Vellie supported me on this path, and I her. For her and my resources, I am grateful.

"Of a Kind"

Vellie's friend who originally encouraged us to meet kept telling her, "You are two of a kind." As we got to know each other, we said the same thing about ourselves. We were happily comfortable together from the first time we met. We are both "creek kids." As children, we inhabited our familiar creeks and surrounding woods. Through our connection with the outdoors and nature, we were nurtured and developed a basic level of health, stability, and grounded connection with our bodies. Our souls were nourished too, by ever-changing and surprising beauty – like the moment I first saw the red budding of a lichen.

Neither of us married and had families in the years when this was the norm for most of our peers. Vellie made no judgments, and she encouraged me to go ahead through serious difficulties in my effort to mature and develop in my work. In our practices in Massachusetts, we shared excitement, curiosity, and continued learning, and when I started the bioenergetic training Vellie was there to support me.

Harmony, Pleasure, and Joy

We enjoyed adventures together with every trip overseas. In Norway and Israel, we walked, skied, drove, and took trains and buses across the remarkable landscapes of these countries. Once, in Israel, we stayed a few days at a guest house of a desert vineyard. The vines were planted along the length of a wadi, a dry stream bed. Using the water technology of the desert people from thousands of years ago, these modern owners made intense red wines fraught with the taste of the desert.

We had the pleasure of being with and working with training groups in both countries, and we felt the depth of their cultural uniqueness. In Norway, Vellie joined me on all the training workshops. She had a lovely, calming presence in the group. People warmed to her kindness and her ability to help them find a way out of their knots. With her presence, the whole task was pleasurable and relaxed for me. The work became a joint endeavor. In Israel, Vellie supervised and did therapy. She listened to me and brought me insight and support.

Our time on Hapardess was not all darkness and demons. Vellie was unfailingly by my side. And even during the many months I was working through my hurts and resentments, I was a constant presence for Vellie and wanted to be with her. During our times of troubles, we supported and took care of each other. During those years, we had a few medical issues, and at those times, we were there for each other.

Contact, Energy, and Love

Our connection answered a deep loneliness in me. The contact I experienced with Vellie was sexual, and it was heart to heart, soul to soul. Vellie's constancy and presence were a healing balm for me during our difficult times. I found joy in holding her and looking into her eyes, which seemed to hold pools of sweetness. Sometimes tears came to my eyes.

In an odd way, I grew up not knowing how to talk with other people. With Vellie, I could talk about my emotions and feel the comfort of her contact. Some of our most important talks happened in the middle of the night. I would wake up preoccupied by one thing or another, and I would get up and sit on the couch in the other room. Often, Vellie woke up and joined me. We sat facing each other, and I talked out what was bothering me.

In all our various conflicts, arguments, upsets, and storms, there was an enormous amount of energy – used, expressed, received, and released. Not all of it was love, but there was love in all of it. The fire generated in my connection with Vellie melted my frozenness and gave me energy for development. It was painful, and it was lifesaving.

As a growing child and adolescent, I usually had little or no appetite. Without knowing what I was experiencing, I was continuously hungry. I seemed to have had some form of anorexia, and inadequate nutrition affected my growth. When we got together, Vellie started putting food on the table. She had never been a cook until then. She chased me out of the kitchen and set to work to learn. That arrangement was a gift and a blessing, as far as I was concerned, and she took care of both of us. Gradually a feeling of nutritional deprivation released its grip on me.

Vellie brought other gifts as well. She felt my intense need for bodily contact. Through thick and thin, there was a basic bodily way in which Vellie was there for me, loving me and allowing me to relax and soften.

Marijuana

While we were living on Hapardess, I discovered that marijuana enhanced the effectiveness of my masturbation seminars, which therefore became known as "m&ms" – masturbation and marijuana. Now they fulfilled the promise I believed the masturbation seminar held when I initiated it.

Marijuana heightened my sexual feeling, and gave me an overall body pleasure, which was a healing experience. By engaging with my experience on the m&m sessions, a change process evolved that continued into the following days and from one time to the next.

Marijuana helped me differentiate difficult feelings and body states (affects) associated with my sexual disturbance. During m&m sessions, I experienced the prohibitions and the shame, humiliation, and self-hate that blocked my sexual feelings. I experienced my dissociation and avoidance, and I experienced self-images associated with sexual ruination. From the quality of my experience, I knew that what I was experiencing was a part of my inner world with sources in the past.

In the days following an m&m, I could track the affects and self-perceptions I experienced during a session and allow them to unfold and evolve. I would talk about my experience with Vellie, follow it in dreams, and do bioenergetic work, producing a multiskeined flow of body affects, memories, feelings, images, and self-perceptions. Such an emotional and somatic-energetic flow is the expression of change happening.

My experience with marijuana made me aware that virtually every negative developmental difficulty had a direct impact on my genital experience and my sense of masculinity. During an m&m session, I experienced in my body the threat to my penis and pelvis. I had perceived the threat as if it were coming from outside of me. So Vellie's anger and rage triggered the feeling of being attacked genitally. This did not reflect her intention or feeling. Now I experienced the feelings of being attacked as something that was already established in my body. It was the effect of frightening childhood experiences. This taking back into myself (re-internalizing) was the basic first step of a healing process. The m&m was a key to freeing myself from my tendency to perceive Vellie as the cause of my injuries, and the threat that had been held in my body gradually faded.

PART VI

Vellie

CHAPTER 21

What Happened to Me?

Questioning

In the early years of my life in the northeast, when I was living alone in Watertown, I had moments of emotional crisis when I called my mother or one of my sisters to see if they could help me with questions I was beginning to ask.

One time I remember clearly, I called my mother. I was sobbing, and I asked her, "Why am I crying like this so often? What happened to me?"

Another time I called my older sister. It was Christmas, and I was alone and sad about not having a family. I asked her, "Why? What happened that my life is so different from yours and our sister's?"

When I called my oldest sister, I asked, "Why have I no memory of a whole time period in my high school years? Why would I not remember?"

Their answers were all the same, "I don't know. I can't think of anything that happened to you that was different."

After a few more half-hearted attempts with similar questions, I decided, "Okay. They can't help me." These were a few

of the first occasions when I asked my family what happened
to me.

Unsettling Experiences

Well before that, in high school, I was having odd, unconnected
experiences, and I became concerned and confused about what
was happening to me. These had to do with academic perfor-
mance. I would read and study for examinations in math and
English grammar, but I would not have a sense that I retained
anything of what I studied. The next day I would take the
exam and make a passing grade. The whole process did not feel
coherent. I had no sense of knowing that I knew what I knew.

I was alone with my worries. I did not think I lacked intelligence, but my difficulties and strange experiences in learning, studying, and taking examinations were confusing and
frightening. I did not have a sense of a mind of my own. I had
to balance that loss by assuring myself that somehow, when I
needed to, I managed to use my mind. It was a long time before
I discovered what it felt like to learn without fear and struggle.

These experiences remained significant memories. When I
was in my thirties, my first therapists did not recognize them as
symptoms of dissociation. Later, when I understood these and
other experiences I mention below as dissociative symptoms,
they gave further credibility and meaning to my question, What
happened to me?

At College

In my first year at college, away from home, I did well, and I
was not troubled by such experiences. However, in my second
year in college, the physical and emotional demands of hospital
nursing training added new kinds of stresses, and I was pushed
close to collapse. We had to be at clinical rounds, dressed in

full uniform, at six thirty in the morning. This meant five-thirty wake-up and breakfast by six. I always made it, but as I sat listening to reports, I would hold my little finger, bend it slightly, and it would be painful. I worried about attending to all the needs of five patients by twelve thirty, when we stopped for lunch and afternoon classes. At the end of the day on Friday I would start crying, and I would cry and sleep most of the weekend.

Before the end of the first semester, the dean called me to her office. "What's going on? Can you continue?" she asked.

I wanted to say, "I don't know." But when I heard her concern, I realized my jeopardy.

I told her, "I cannot stop. I must continue. I do not have a choice."

Following some discussion, we agreed I would continue.

After this meeting, the faculty arranged a medical checkup for me. I was in the hospital for two days and tests revealed I had a serious hypothyroid condition. My coping capacities had been stressed beyond their limit, and my resilience was limited.

The attention of the faculty and their intervention was a major boost, giving me a sense of support and a feeling of safety, and I knew I could continue. With medication, my energy revived, and I took on my student nursing work with more strength and resilience.

At the end of the four years, I took state exams for registration in nursing, and – to my great relief – I passed on the first try. I persisted, and I succeeded! Now I felt secure in being able to make a living and support myself.

Psychotherapy

A few months after I moved to Boston, I started psychotherapy with an analytic psychiatrist. I was thirty-one, and I saw him for two years. I had ideals and convictions about the importance of psychotherapy, so just the ritual of going gave me some support. However, he sat and listened and rarely responded. He and other therapists I knew of at that time were limited in their understanding of trauma and the developmental problems I was living with. I did not get the help I needed with my feelings, and this therapy did not address my question, What happened to me? I do not remember how I ended the therapy.

In the years before I got together with Phil, I remained dedicated to trying to find good psychotherapy. But I encountered two sexually disturbed therapists: one during long-term therapy, and one in a week-long workshop. On both occasions, I attempted to ward off unwanted and confusing advances; but left with the vulnerabilities of my adolescence, I was not able to hold my ground and protect myself. My trust was betrayed, and this made subsequent therapeutic development difficult. This was nearly fifty years ago, and few, if any, therapists were aware of or had a natural understanding of the depth of the problem I faced. Again, I was alone with my pain and guilt.

Two other therapists, who had been helpful initially, also disrupted my work with them due to their limited development as therapists. At crucial points, when I was most distressed, they both failed me by their lack of empathy, and responded punitively. Feeling stronger, I ended my work with them.

More than ten years later, I made the decision to work with a reputable psychoanalyst in the Boston area. During an initial period, I found the work with him to be supportive. As I reached deeper into my sexual confusion and trauma, he responded with clever interpretations that felt lifeless to me and must have expressed his anxiety about sexuality and my emotions. This time, I quickly knew that I needed to leave this therapy. I made one more attempt with a woman therapist, but because

I had lost trust I could not engage with a psychotherapist in productive work.

My question, "What happened to me?" came back into focus; its meaning evolved over the next years, and through that evolution it came to be answered in ways I had not anticipated. I made the decision to focus on my relationship with Phil and the self-study work we were doing. I gained a deeper understanding that I was dealing with symptoms of dissociation and that these were the effects of traumatic experiences from my childhood and adolescence. This is a common understanding now, but in those years, we were on our own in catching on to the pioneering work in the field of trauma theory and therapy and working it out for ourselves. For me, this meant finding ways and opportunities to restore, build, and be myself by repairing the destructive effects of the traumas I had been living with.

Trauma is an experience, not an event. So, "What happened to me?" now had a clearer and more specific meaning. What were the experiences that led to the development of my symptoms of dissociation? There was some essential answer to this question that was missing. I knew *when* something had happened (my last two years in high school), but not *what* it was. I felt an urgent necessity to find the memory or memories that would answer this question. But I couldn't find them, and this left me desperate (this situation is discussed in Chapter 23, "Dissociation").

As finding answers to that question became more urgent, I experienced the uncertainty and ambiguity that I was left in without having answers. I came to accept this state as my fate, and as I did so, the urgency of the question calmed down. As I realized I was capable of living with ambiguity, I came to see that I had been answering my question all along, with a different meaning. When Phil and I began to write our reports, I was writing down all the things that had "happened to me" as a result of my childhood and adolescent traumas. These are the symptoms of dissociation and posttraumatic disorder that I describe in this chapter and elsewhere. This is what happened to me.

As I understood and accepted these traits for what they are, I was able to look more deeply into their cause. These explorations are described in the final chapters.

CHAPTER 22

Connecting With Phil

In my twenties and thirties, marrying and having children was an ideal, but I did not engage with that ideal in a way that would make it a reality. I could consider marriage only in a vague way in relation to the man who might be in my life at the time

I was sexually excited about Phil when I first met him, and for me, that was the start of our connection. When we became a couple, ten years after we first met, I did not evaluate what kind of relationship might now develop. A love relationship or how love could develop did not occur to me. I expected to be with him as we had been together before. And that was the same way I had been with the other men in my life. Sadly, I had never made a commitment, I maintained my sense of freedom, and I could not consider marriage in a realistic way. My experience with Phil turned out to be entirely different, and the many new, intense experiences I encountered gave me further reason to question what had happened to me.

There was an "as if" quality about me as I lived our relationship. I lacked a depth of feeling. My emotional connection with myself was still partially dissociated, and I was left unable to make a deeper connection with another.

The *as if* state made it difficult for me to know what I wanted and to be consistently available for active response in daily life or sex. Undoubtedly, that created difficulties for Phil and must have contributed to his frequent upsets and anger with me. I sometimes viewed him as a monster when he was like that, and I would wonder why I would want to stay with him.

When I did not experience a connection or love, I had all the more reason to question staying with him. I did experience a loving connection, but holding on to the connection was difficult for me. When I lost it, I did not know how to get it back. So, in my experience, our connection would come and go, creating a confusing situation for me. Sometimes I could remind myself of my loving feelings for him, and trusted staying with him based on those remembered feelings.

We had a strong connection. And I see the extent to which – even as I lived it – I was often in conflict. One day, we were outside at our house in Pepperell. Phil was stacking wood. I was sitting on a tree stump near where he was working, and I was crying almost hysterically.

I was saying to Phil, "I can't do this. I cannot do a relationship. I do not know why, but it's too, too painful and frightening."

I was also frantic at the thought that we might not be able to stay together. The conflict of these two frightening states was painful and distressing.

The years with Phil and all our experiences together are beyond important. The amazing amount of time we took for discussions and talks about our conflicts and struggles, how to hold contact with ourselves and each other, our intelligent use of drug trips, and our self-study work gave me what I needed to start developing a sense of self-respect and self-agency. Throughout all these experiences I gradually gained the capacity to sustain excitement and my loving feelings, which gave me the strength to hold our connection.

CHAPTER 23

Dissociation

Father's Caretaker

When I was seventeen to eighteen, my junior and senior high school years, I developed symptoms of dissociation. Some of these were behaviors and some were ways I experienced myself and the events of my life. When I looked at my life history in later years, I could see that whatever caused these symptoms hurt me deeply as a young woman, and left injuries that interfered with my development and functioning for most of my life.

During this time, my parents' schedules enabled them to avoid each other week after week. They were living separately but staying in the home. My father had a job as a night watchman in a creosote factory, and my mother continued her teaching. This allowed her to leave before he returned home in the morning, and he would leave before she returned home in the afternoon. On weekends he visited his parents and sisters. I do not recall having any thoughts or feelings of concern about their situation.

This separation may have worked for them, but it did

not work for me. They decided it was my job to be at home after school to get my father off to work. Mother prepared the meal he was to have before leaving for work and left it in the refrigerator. My job was to set it out for him and make his coffee. It was a family joke that he could not get his own dinner, "because the dishes were covered, so he could not see what was in them." I also put together his nighttime lunch with things my mother organized, and I was to check to see if Mother left out his clean clothes. Sometimes I had to iron his khaki shirts and pants because he insisted on having them fresh every day, even for this night job. Although he wore overalls over them, all his clothing had the offensive odor of the factory.

My father's need and entitlement to having these simple chores taken care of for him were never questioned. He had been the recipient of this level of caretaking all his life. Now, at a time when my mother would not comply with this arrangement, they settled the jobs upon me. Since this was a necessity, as far as they were concerned, the fact that I had to give up the after-school life I needed for myself did not enter the equation.

I have a few specific, conscious memories from that period, but what I do recall still leaves huge gaps. I do know that my father's emotional functioning was actively disturbed at this time. And I know that my numbness, blankness and "not knowing" were outcomes of whatever happened to me during this period.

My Father: An Introduction

My father was born and raised in Louisiana and lived in the vicinity of his birth all his life. One day in a bioenergetic workshop I was asked to describe my father. One word came out of my mouth: "Ignorant." I was surprised. I had never said that before or even thought about him in that light.

The traumas that deeply disturbed my development, especially my sexual development as a teenager, occurred in my relationship with him. (This is not to imply that my relationship with my mother was benign; it was not.) As I explored my sexual development over the years, I came to see that my father was immature, lacking in empathy, and sexually disturbed. He was present day to day, but he was emotionally flat, and hardly communicative. I saw and experienced his rage, and I think his family and my mother did too, but no one acknowledged it.

Growing up, I heard his family tell a peculiar story about him. He had five sisters; he was the oldest child and the only son. The story relates how my father would go into a rage any time one of his sisters wanted to go out on a date. On one occasion, when one of his sisters did go on a date, his wrath led to breaking a hole in a wall. This story and others were told as if they reflected virtue, as if he were protecting his sisters.

He attempted to act the same way with my older sisters, but my mother protected them by setting limits and boundaries on how much ho could be involved. On the few occasions in my teen years when I was interested in a boy and my father knew of it, he went into a rage. My mother was not around at those times, and when she did know of the problem for me, she would not intervene.

I have only a few memories of activities he did with me and my sisters. He would drive us to our various activities and usually be there for them. He was present in my life, so I always felt I had a father, and that was supportive in itself. Some of my friends' families did not have that. But when he was with us, he did not make an emotional connection with me as a person.

A Child's Love Stopped

My dissociative state very nearly derailed my education. It had a disastrous effect on my developing sexuality.

I have always remembered an experience with my father from around age four that deeply hurt me and had a traumatic impact on my capacity for excitement and love.

In my memory, I am sitting on my father's lap feeling excited and feeling my love for him.

He cajoled me into saying, "I love you more than I love my mother."

Then he called my mother into the room and told her what I said. She looked terribly angry. I slid off his lap, and I remember feeling frightened and aware that something bad just happened. I felt frightened by my mother's anger and that it was my fault. I felt another kind of pain because of my father's laughter. His actions were cruel, betrayed my love for him, and supported the beginnings of my fear of excitement and love. Of course, I did not know the words "betrayal" and "excitement," but I did experience a kind of pain that remained with me. It is a memory I described to my first therapists.

Previously I described the period when I slept in the same room with my parents. I cringe at the thought that, as a small child, I was exposed to their intimate life every night for three years. I must have been exposed to the sounds of activities and conversations that stimulated sensations I would not have been able to understand and that would have disturbed me. In these circumstances, blocking awareness of my bodily reactions would have been natural and automatic. Whatever impression of sexual activity I acquired from this experience cast a shadow over my developing sexuality.

After that shadowed time, my feelings started to come back alive again from the age of nine. We were in our own home, and I was sharing a bedroom with my two sisters, far away from my parents' bedroom. During these years, I made friends, enjoyed school, and enjoyed having boyfriends. I loved going to summer camps where we had the opportunity to be kids and do the fun things kids in the South did at that time.

Later in this period, when I was thirteen, there was the ice cream party incident when I had my "almost" first date. My father's crazy rage crushed my young sexual excitement at this time (see Chapter 6, "My Life Opens").

Two Fateful Years

When I changed to the ew high school at the beginning of my junior year, I was happy, and excited at meeting new classmates. I was ready to be free to have my excitement and enjoy my experiences as a teenage girl. Between classes one sunny, warm fall afternoon, typical for Louisiana, I was sitting in a big circle on a grassy lawn with my two best girlfriends and some others. A boy who I had just met came and sat down next to me. He seemed excited to talk with me. Before long he was suggesting we "go steady," and he gave me his ring.

A few days later, my father crushed my excitement. The day the boy gave me his ring, I took it home and proudly threaded it on a black velvet ribbon to wear around my neck. When my father noticed it a few days later, he frightened me with his anger, and demanded I take it off and give it back to the boy.

When I told my mother about his anger and demands, she shrugged and told me I should do as he said. I was hoping for some intervention and support, but sadly there was none. I returned the ring the next day, mumbling something about my father not allowing me to keep it. The important connection with the boy ended and injured my hope to be free to have my excitement.

My mother's shrug was painfully disheartening, as if she were saying, "I don't want to bother with you."

I was liked at school, but that is different from having the pleasurable excitement of adolescence and dating. Now, the hopes I had when I began the year closed, and I made sure not to draw attention to myself. Painful to recall, I would no longer even notice the boy who gave me the ring.

For the remainder of those two years, when other boys asked me for dates, I always gave answers that basically said, "No," and after that I avoided them as much as possible. With one persistent boy, I finally gave in and went out with him. I was angry and sullen out of my fear of being on a date. He did not ask me again.

I did regular adolescent activities with my girlfriends, like listening to records and going to the drug store and drinking cherry Coke. I was not a regular adolescent like them in that I did not date or have a boyfriend, but I thought that would happen sometime. I started thinking of myself as shy and quiet, and my friends saw me in the same way, so it became my identity and the norm for me.

My father persisted in crushing my excitement. One day, not long after the ring episode, I was walking home with a group of boys and girls, all laughing and talking. We were crossing the meadow near our house where my father was trying to sleep because of his night job.

He threw open a window and, still in his underwear, shouted at us, "Shut up!"

I froze, turned away from my new friends, and walked across to my home. When I opened the door to go in, he was behind the door and closed the door after me. As far as I can remember, what happened next was that he was in a rage with me. Following this event, I avoided anything faintly suggesting excitement, fun, or pleasure that involved boys. I would ruminate and look at some boy who I wished would notice me and find me attractive, but I would not respond to boys who expressed any interest in being with me.

Punishment

Many times over the years, when Phil encouraged me to talk about my father, I was triggered into a state of fear in which I had the experience of actual blows – as if I were being beaten – across my shoulders and back. I could almost feel the physical impact, and it frightened me. I was horrified as I would describe this phantom beating to Phil.

I am not entirely sure how to account for this phantom experience. Gradually over the years, I could sense the feelings of having done something wrong and that I was a bad person. What I do know is that there were crucial moments when my father reacted with rage when he discovered any sign I had responded to or received attentions from a boy. I do not remember my father physically hitting me. However, his reactions to noticing any signs of my excitement were violent expressions.

My father's behavior with me took unbearable turns. For one thing, he took it upon himself to sit reading his paper in a chair that I had to pass by on my way out to school. He would evaluate my appearance, check my clothes and shoes, and sometimes insist I make changes. To avoid conflict, I resigned myself to wearing the few items I knew would pass his inspection. He made sure I never wore anything that might even remotely draw attention to my sexual attractiveness, like a peasant blouse with a slight low cut that had been a favorite. He would add his criticisms of my shoes and repeat over and over that my feet were large and unattractive.

On Saturday mornings during this time, I found myself staying in bed, lying awake, feeling I could not move. My mother occasionally came in to check on me, and once or twice she brought a woman friend from the neighborhood. They looked at me and laughed about "lazy adolescents." Calling me lazy was completely ignoring the after-school responsibilities she had turned over to me and that I was fulfilling every school day. Neither did she note my bland and blank responses.

I am accounting for my symptoms of dissociation. Earlier experiences had moved me in this direction, but my dissociation was locked in during this period. What happened during those two years put my subsequent survival as a person in constant jeopardy. As problematic as my development had been up until then, my life difficulties would have been much reduced if I had been spared the worst of these years. My life had been forever changed.

Although I had my friends and my adolescent activities, I felt alone. My parents, of course, were not paying enough attention to see what was happening to me, and besides, *they* were what was happening to me! I fondly remember kindly teachers who noticed me and helped me prepare for college.

CHAPTER 24

Body Numbing

I told my first therapists that I often felt numb, immobilized, and that at those times I had little feeling. In later years of pursuing self-study, I became aware of what I was *not* feeling and of the peculiarly disconnected quality of what I *did* feel. I experienced numbness, and sometimes I could *observe* myself doing something *as if* I had a clear motivation, but one I did not connect with. I often felt that Phil's upsetness and anger with me was the only way someone was going to reach me and stir something in me that had to be awakened or brought to life.

I learned to view an *as if* pattern of behavior as *reliving* – that is, reliving a traumatic experience, or some aspect of it, from my past. This (dissociative) tendency was not always present. Many of my life experiences were entirely real to me.

Once I became aware that, at times, I was living a dissociative, *as if* life, I had to learn to pay attention to exactly what I *was* experiencing. With attention, the *as if* condition would resolve into my real feelings. Affects and feelings that had been split from my sense of self became integrated aspects of myself.

My life with Phil provided a great portion of my learning experiences. With him, I kept "finding myself" feeling and doing things that hardly seemed like me. They were experiences of a sort I had not had before. I did not know where they came from, and they were disturbing – and suggested that I was disturbed. These experiences carried the demand that I look at myself, question, and explore.

From the time I first got together with Phil as a couple, the stresses of being in an intimate relationship with him repeatedly triggered me into intense episodes of pain, conflict, and turmoil. Over several years, I experienced emotions and behaviors that were unknown to me.

In the earlier years of our relationship, just being in close connection with Phil set me into acute alertness to any faint hint of being blamed or accused, a possibility that was constantly alive in me. If I picked up any mild indication of such a possibility, I would immediately feel as if I were in a dangerous conflict. Instantly, I could become frantic with fear. The frantic feelings and behavior were unknown to me; I had never been in a relationship where I reacted that way. And what is worse, I felt humiliated to be exposed acting as I was, making the situation all the more untenable for me.

In such situations, I soon found myself struggling through an elaborate defensive protocol that could not be shifted. Not being at fault became my truth, a truth I would not relinquish easily, maintaining it as a position for hours or days. The tension, conflict, and arousal all made a situation like this feel dangerous to me. Often, I had to escape. Occasionally, in the winter in Pepperell, I sheltered under the low, snow-covered boughs of my large, protective hemlock. I found safety in small spaces. They held me quietly, calming my fear of losing control, and offered a boundary to help me gather myself and quiet down.

The episodes with Phil involved terrible states of being – suffering, rage, terror, inner turmoil, and the frightening feeling of being on the edge of losing control. I experienced all those states as real-time events and as being caused by Phil's behavior. When I felt blamed or dropped, I "knew" Phil was the perpetrator, doing something to me that caused me to feel that way. When I was frantic, terrified, or in a rage, it had to be because of Phil. When I felt alone and like dying, it was because of Phil's abandonment.

Before I was with Phil, I had never had the experience of feeling the victim at the hands of a perpetrator, although there were a few vague hints of these feelings with other relationships. Now I was the suffering, enraged victim, trapped in the connection with her perpetrator. In the thick of one of these episodes, this is how I was. I was in the sea of woe, and peace and love were nowhere to be seen. I could not even dream of how to get from where I was to some other better place. Not only did I not know how to get there, sadly, at these times, I could not even imagine there was another place.

I did, however, have enough of my self – enough of a self – to gradually find a solid place to return to, from which, once again, I was able to continue learning how to get from here to there. I was able to calm down, reaffirm my commitment to fulfilling my wish for connection and love, and come back to my love and faith in Phil. I returned to the reality of now.

There was one particular truth that was necessary for both of us to learn. We each had to have that key to unlock the last obstacles to being able to find happiness with each other. Forces in our inner worlds kept us from this truth for a long time. I came to understand that no matter what Phil had done, it did not warrant my extremes of feelings and behavior. He frequently did one or another of the hurtful things he has described himself doing. Still, what he did was not a warrant for my extreme, frantic, out-of-control states. *This understanding is that basic key.*

I learned that my questionable behaviors, which I perceived as caused by Phil, came from within me, from my inner world. This learning brought my question – "What happened to me?" – into clear focus. Because something had to have happened to leave behind the horror inside me that created so much pain and disturbance in my life.

This same key opens the way to freedom. When I no longer claim, "It is because of you that I suffer," I am owning my experience, and I am independent of you. I am free.

CHAPTER 25

My Way

Moving On After College

After I began self-study, I learned that "my way" meant moving on whenever a relationship became too close, in order to avoid intimacy and remain alone. My enjoyment of being alone and free began before I started school, when I was a small child, playing outside by myself. I have vague memories of playing alone, free to explore the nooks and crannies around the house, as long as I did not leave the fenced-in yard. My older sisters were in school, and I was home with my mother. In the afternoon, I waited for my sisters, who often did not come home right away, because they stopped at our grandmother's house for milk and her great sugar cookies. Sometimes my mother and I met them there, but usually it seemed like a long wait, and I longed to be with them, doing what they were doing.

As I got older, when we were at my maternal grandmother's, my solitary explorations were more extensive. I would quietly amble out of the house along my path and down to the creek. In the summer, dust, crickets, and other interesting bugs would fly up as I walked, leaving the lasting impression that I recalled later in life, the smell of the dust, the sounds, and especially the strong feelings of freedom, being out of the house and alone.

By the time I finished college, my way was firmly established. As soon as I finished my degree and passed my nursing boards, I made plans to leave Louisiana. I decided I wanted to go to Denver to experience the mountains and enjoy winter sports. I informed my parents, but I did not ask for their help with my plans or for financial support. This was 1958–1959, and I was twenty-two. I ambled out of the South to the mountains of Colorado.

I stayed almost a year in Denver. I learned to ski, and I met people from all over the world. My awareness of the world expanded, and my experiences started the movement that took me out of the tribal culture of my family and the South. I was searching for a path that would free me from *the something* – that something that was the trauma that had stopped me in my development.

Chicago

After Denver, I spent two years with my parents in Louisiana. During that time, I was engaged to Luke. When my engagement ended (see Chapter 11, "My Life with Men"), with barely a second breath, I made plans to leave Louisiana. I made my plans and left – this time for Chicago (I did not amble; this time I fast walked out of the South).

In Chicago, I regained my enjoyment of meeting new people and having new life experiences. I loved my time there, including the windy, cold, snowy winters. I began the life of a single young woman, age twenty-five. To my surprise I had frequent dates – a movie, a football game, or parties. I enjoyed the dating life. Now I could experience the pleasure of being held and being sexual, the natural feelings for a young woman my age. At the same time, my sexual experience also gave me a glimpse of my immaturity and lack of a capacity for deeper feelings with another. This was my first conscious intimation that my sexual self had been deeply injured, and remembering her now, I feel compassion for myself as that twenty-five-year-old.

My experience of being alone and of being with others was changing. I had a longing to be with people and a longing to be alone, a polarity that had been part of me all through my childhood and adolescence. I still preferred to be alone, but now I was affected by the loss of my family, which left me feeling more separate and somewhat uprooted. So, I was motivated to test myself socially, but being with others impinged on the carefully maintained boundary that protected me from being overwhelmed. I moved the boundary bar so there was some expansion, but I continued to find ways to maintain my safety.

My experience during my two years in Chicago fostered my development into adulthood. I discovered that I could be the one to choose my partner. I felt comfortable and safe with one young man who was a little older, a psychiatrist, and we were together for about a year. The moment he started talking about love and marriage, I was immediately gripped by my familiar need to move on, keep my freedom, and remain alone.

The drive to be alone had evolved and was now moving me toward the dangerous territory of rejecting love, resulting in my remaining isolated in aloneness. I was not conscious of the motives behind my decision, and I did not stop to question myself. Even so, being with a man I chose for nearly a year was a big step.

There was another factor that interfered with my being able to have my excitement and know the pleasure of sexual love. I came to see that I had been harmed and confused by growing up under the influence of the church teaching about sex. I described before how I had learned early that excitement, sex, and Hell were all related. A corollary to this teaching was used to control girls and young women in the 1950s, especially in the South. By that corollary, I was to believe that the girl or young woman who is excited about men will be looked on as a whore. Yes! That is the word, that horrible word. These beliefs made me anxious and added to my fear about sexual desire.

Father's Illness and Death

My time of freedom in Chicago ended when I learned that my father had cancer. He needed someone to be his treatment coordinator. I was the nurse, and I was single, so the job fell to me. Once again, I returned to Louisiana and devoted more than a year to organizing his treatment and care and being involved with my family at this painful time, the last year of my father's life.

During the years 1964 to 1965 I made my home in New Orleans, where my father received his chemotherapy. New Orleans itself is an experience and being there allowed me to manage my life my way. I had the freedom I would not have had in the family home, and I loved living in the French Quarter, only a block from Bourbon Street. Going to work was a pleasure every day, because I could either walk to work through the historic part of the city, or I could ride the charming streetcars along Canal Street. I enjoyed visits with friends from Chicago who were eager to experience New Orleans and Mardi Gras, and we listened to jazz in the world-famous Preservation Hall.

Less than a year after my father died, my mother had a medical crisis. I left New Orleans, moved in with Mother to look after her, and worked in nearby hospitals. Months later we learned she was not at risk. By this time, I had been in

Louisiana for more than three years looking after my parents. I had been dreaming about traveling in Europe for a long time. Now I felt free to plan my trip.

Traveling: New England and Europe

I planned to drive to New Hampshire and stay with friends before leaving for Europe. As I drove north towards Washington, DC, leaving one Southern state after the other, I approached the Mason-Dixon line, the historical boundary dividing the South from the North during the Civil War. As I passed through this territory, I began crying and the crying soon became sobbing. I knew I was leaving the South forever, and that meant I was leaving my family and the culture of my childhood. I felt the loss and grieved from the depths of my heart.

My friends met me in DC and accompanied me the rest of the way. I stayed with them for three weeks, gratefully receiving much-needed care. During these weeks, I realized that I was emotionally shaky, and the thought of a trip to Europe was overwhelming.

I got a job in Boston and started my life in the Boston-Cambridge area of Massachusetts.

Four years later, I was ready to go to Europe, and I planned a five-month trip. At the time I left Boston, the man I was seeing, Ben, had been carefully hinting at a wish for commitment. This probably stimulated my movement to get away. Despite the fact that we had been seeing each other for three years, I made my plans without involving him, leaving him puzzled and hurt. When I returned, we resumed seeing each other, but our relationship had changed.

At the time, I viewed my European trip as another life adventure. It gave me a great deal of pleasure, and I was excited by how rich the experience was and how much I learned about

European culture. Traveling *my way* meant that most of the time I was alone. I saw myself as a person who felt good about being alone and free to go about my days without the difficulties of a relationship or even a close friendship.

I was thirty-four when I went to Europe. I look back on myself as a thirty-four-year-old woman, and I feel sad for how undeveloped I was, even at that age. I was still doing life *my way*, and I was alone. Being alone, I felt free, but sadly, I had not yet become aware of my fear of intimacy and my deficit in the capacity for love in a relationship. I was running from any experience that might elicit such awareness. I had not let myself in on the reality that by always getting out and moving on, I was escaping and running from *something*. For me, at that time in my life, this was a loss.

CHAPTER 26

"I Don't Know"

Not Knowing

Phil and I became aware that I said it time and again: "I don't know. I don't know. I don't know." Often, when asked to respond to a question about a decision or a feeling, my immediate, automatic answer was, "I don't know."

I wanted to communicate with Phil in a natural way, expressing my thoughts and feelings, but sometimes I did not know how. I would fall back on a tactic that had served me all my life, which was checking out the other person. On these occasions with Phil, I would look intensely at his face and eyes and say, "You are feeling … about me. That's what is making it impossible for me to feel what I'm feeling."

He would say, "No. You can't do that. You can't tell me what you feel based on what you think I feel." He called what I was doing "making attributions."

Then I would feel stuck in my own struggle. I had to acknowledge, at least as a starter, that sometimes I really did not know how to express my own thoughts and feelings.

Sometimes, to soften my apparent discomfort, Phil would

joke in a kindly way, "You're 'the I don't know girl,'" or he would find some way to tell me it was okay not to know.

There were times when I believed I *should* know. These were times when I had the most difficulty knowing what I felt, such as identifying and expressing angry feelings, or what was even more painful, when I wanted to reach out for help and contact. I would become frantic if it were a situation where Phil was pressuring me to respond to him because he was angry. In that frantic state I would search around in my consciousness desperately looking for something, anything, to express a feeling.

The most difficult feeling for me was when I felt I had done something wrong; *it was all my fault.* Then I would come up with *something* that I might conceivably have done wrong and confess to it. Having found something I could feel wrong about, I reflexively dropped into a long, unhappy process of soul-searching, in an effort to change that *something* in myself that was wrong. I made use of all my psychological knowledge in what amounted to a self-excoriation. This seemed to be the only way I knew how to cope with this awful state of feeling at fault.

My self-excoriation went beyond reasonable bounds. It served only to make me miserable and feel helpless and frustrated. If the process went on, I could collapse into a terrible state of self-hate. I would look for ways to get relief from the pain I was in, and sometimes anger would be the way out. That was frightening when I had the need to turn it on Phil, because I knew it would only increase the conflict and my pain.

Just at a point like this, Phil might come out with, "Are you angry with me?"

That would be just the thing that released my anger, and it would go toward him. Sooner or later, I would have to settle down and go back to the simple, sad fact that at the start of all this, I just did not know what I felt.

And, sad to say, I *did not know*. This can be a terrible state to be in, especially when trying to relate to someone. I understand now that my difficulty was not *what* I did not know, the issue was my *state* of not knowing. When I became aware of my *bodily* experience of this state, then I could understand the difference between not knowing *something* and the state of not knowing, which is a state of *being*.

Blank

Being blank was another typical, frequent experience. At times I would say, "I don't know," and at other times I would just be blank – no content, no feeling, no thoughts, just blank. I was likely to go blank at times of utmost importance to me. The most painful of such moments is wanting badly to feel and share excitement with Phil when he approached me with excitement. Becoming aware of the blankness, I felt sad and disturbed.

Over the years I learned about the connection between not knowing and blankness. They both resulted from the numbing that was an outcome of my childhood experience. As a child I learned to rely on these states to alleviate my distress.

Sexual Development

The same traumatic developments that resulted in my not knowing and my blankness also caused my sexual numbing. A prosaic example from my high school years graphically illustrates and symbolizes the disturbance in my sexual development.

For an adolescent girl, the way she dresses for formal school events is a serious matter. My example has to do with the way I dressed when I attended our "Junior-Senior Evening," which was like a formal dinner.

In my junior year, I made my appearance dressed in a sexy, strapless bandeau cocktail dress (belonging to my oldest sister), and I made a big hit. The following year at the same event, I showed up in an odd puffy net dress that hid my sexual attractiveness as much as possible, so I did not receive the attention of the boys in my class.

The difference between these two dresses graphically symbolizes what happened to my sexual development and that resulted in my learning to hide my sexuality. The overall effects on my life are far more consequential than what I wore to a high school social event. But these two events are time markers: between them, whatever I experienced left a traumatic impact.

I know that my life as a woman has been, and still is, seriously compromised. When I got together with Phil, I was forty-three. I had not married or started a family, and I had never lived with a partner. A relationship of twelve years had ended before Phil and I became a couple, and I had been in other long-term relationships. Once Phil and I became a couple, painful difficulties arose again and again. I had never attempted the kind of intimacy that we wanted with each other, and now, when I did, I opened a Pandora's box.

In my journey with Phil, I gradually focused more and more on my personal development in an effort to free myself. I had to alleviate depression caused by the numbing, calm down rage, and quiet the states of upset that were frequently triggered. My life and work have been dedicated to freeing myself of pain and suffering. The freeing of my energy, the discovery of my self, and the development of my capacity for love are the momentous outcomes of our efforts.

PART VII

Vellie

CHAPTER 27

Learning to Be With

A Child Alone

All through my early years I enjoyed being with my friends at school and in my neighborhood. And I felt quite happy playing or reading a book with one of my sisters. But I had another side of myself too. I was at ease being alone and enjoyed time by myself. I especially enjoyed being outdoors by myself. When there was tension between my parents, I felt uneasy, so being outside was freedom from being in the house with them.

There were happy times when my sisters and I would be in the kitchen with our mother making dinner, and we sang songs. Each of us, including Mother, had a solo part. Singing our solos and then singing the chorus together, all the while making dinner, was fun, and I loved it when we were all together.

By the time I was an adult, I was most at home in the alone side of myself. So after graduating from college as a nurse, I left Louisiana without misgivings, and I was comfortable living on my own for a year in Denver. I also felt comfortable with the two other departures from my home in Louisiana, first for

Chicago and then for Boston.

I felt good about being alone through many of my years as a single woman. My women friends were fun, and we shared many experiences. I had relationships with men who were quiet, somewhat solitary people. My involvement with them did not have the active intimacy and depth of feeling that would have stimulated me to recognize I needed to do something about my sexual and emotional immaturity. Longing was not a feeling I identified in myself for many years.

Learning the Basics

When Phil and I got together as a couple, I believed I was responding to a similar quality in him. I thought of him as enjoying solitude, living a quiet life in the country. I discovered that "quiet" was only one side of him. The first time he got upset and angry with me, I was taken off guard, and did not have a response.

Once we were together, I had to start learning the basics of being with another person. I experienced frequent, intense conflicts when we were upset and disappointed in each other, and I had to find the strength to listen and let go of my defensive positions as well as hold my own ground. It also took time for me to learn to reach out to him during a conflict and not withdraw. To be happy with Phil, I had to take care of myself in a way that eventually allowed me to safely maintain my self-respect.

As time went on, I wanted to be with him more, and I finally took what, for me, was the giant step of moving in with him in his house in Pepperell. This allowed me to be with him more during the week; but I also kept my small condo to escape to when I needed alone time.

I wanted to be with Phil, but I felt that we were causing each other to be hurt and upset much too often. There were any number of times when I had to stand up for myself or get away from him. One of the most painful and difficult of those times occurred when we were on vacation in Newfoundland.

Phil described this event in one of his chapters, and I want to describe what I now know to be the part of me that triggered Phil's disturbance. I can describe it simply. From childhood I have had a characteristic manner of holding myself back emotionally, preserving the alone space inside me. When we were on a vacation, where we could be together in a strong intimate way, that behavior and space was there and dynamically alive, even though I was not aware of it. Of course, when Phil wanted to be sexually intimate with me, he encountered my holding back and my inner aloneness on a bodily, nonverbal level, and he experienced it as a lack of response to him and a rejection of his excitement. This was upsetting in the worst way for him.

In Newfoundland, we made love that first night. In the morning, when we were taking up our tent, we were talking, and I was feeling excited about our pleasurable plans for the trip. When we got in the car after breakfast, I had a wonderful, cozy feeling.

I said, "I'm going to curl up in my seat, enjoy the warmth of the sun, and maybe doze a few minutes."

Just as I was settling into my corner, Phil suddenly blew up in a rage. I had no idea why he became so upset and angry with me. And I do not think he did either, except to say he felt left.

I got incredibly angry and upset. No thoughts preceded my reaction. I felt something was finished. I could not manage having this kind of rage directed at me. I decided to end the relationship. For the remainder of the vacation, I refused to share a hotel room with him.

Only many years later could I understand that my lack of awareness of my unresponsiveness might have been a trigger for his outburst. At the time, of course, I did not have that awareness.

After we got home from the vacation, Phil cried and suffered for three or four weeks, while I was unrelenting in my determination that I would never, ever be yelled at again. After these painful weeks, I acknowledged that I cared and wanted to stay with him. I had reached another level of experiencing how to be with another. I had found the strength to set a boundary for myself even if it meant separating, and at the same time, I could feel the longing to be with him.

A Time of Trial

We did have long periods of pleasure and enjoyment together. But it often seemed that every week, or every other week, we would have an upsetting, painful time. We wanted to find a path or a way of life that would make it possible to be together with love, pleasure, and peace.

There was another occasion, many years after our Newfoundland vacation, when I resolved that I could no longer remain in the relationship as it was. However, this time, I did not feel I wanted to leave Phil. On this occasion, I was again feeling accused of creating a terrible, upsetting disturbance, when I felt that I had done nothing that deserved such accusations. This time, it started when we were in Watertown, just before moving to our new home in Kfar Saba, Israel. The disturbance spanned the whole time of finishing our preparations and clearing out our house. Then there was further disturbance once we began moving into our new home in Israel, up to a final point of implosion and explosion. It was a terrible time.

This is how it came about. Phil had participated in a weekend workshop where he had a very painful, but important experience in a group with people not associated with our work, and two or three weekends after that, he taught a training workshop. On that weekend, I spent a long time on the telephone with an old friend, and the conversation left me upset and disturbed.

When Phil came home from his long and satisfying weekend of work, he wanted to let down, relax, and enjoy being with me. I was upset, anxious, and disturbed, and I needed to talk about the conversation with my friend.

I started talking after supper. I could not stop, and I was not coming to any resolution. Phil reached a point where he got upset listening to me. My tension then got focused between us. I panicked and could not calm down. Phil asked me to come to bed, breathe, and be with him until I could relax some. I did that.

I still felt anxious and upset. When I thought he was asleep, I went into the other room to lie on a blanket roll, breathe, and attempt to get in touch with what had upset me. This is my familiar way of working with panic and anxiety, and usually it helps me allow my anxiety to pass through.

Suddenly Phil came in from the bedroom. He was standing over me and I felt him yelling at me. He was saying, "What in the world is wrong with you?"

I said, "I'm breathing and trying to find out."

What else was said, I do not know. But I heard him say I was being "imbecilic."

That word horrified me. I looked up, and I saw anger on his face and what I assumed was hate.

Then words came out of my mouth, and they were, "Why don't you go ahead and kill me. Get it over with."

Those words horrified Phil and sent him back to bed to try to quiet himself. Gradually I quieted down and went to bed. For the next two or three days, while getting things prepared to move to Israel, I kept trying to find some way to understand the word "imbecilic," and thinking that maybe my anxiety and panic was some imbecilic way of being. I was disturbed; I could not let it go. But we had to get focused and get ready to go, which we did.

Resolve Out of Brokenness

I was excited about moving to Israel, now as a citizen. After a day of signing papers, we got the keys to our new home. It was a beautiful place. We started setting it up for our pleasure and for living and working there. We decided to go down to the old town market and buy a table, which was also an exciting adventure.

I drove back to our apartment, followed by the man bringing the table in his truck. I was anxious driving in the heavily trafficked Israeli roads. I told Phil I was anxious and was focusing on my breathing. In case he became suddenly aware of my tension, I wanted him to know I was aware, and I was okay.

Phil said, "Just breathe!" in an irritated voice.

I said I was breathing, but what I heard in his voice triggered in me what I had been left with when I heard the word "imbecilic." Again, I became extremely upset. For our safety, I stayed focused and quiet until we could get home. Phil had to cope with the delivery and wrangling the table into an elevator to get it up to our place, which was difficult and upsetting for him.

This series of events – from the word "imbecilic" to the stressful trip for a table – was the beginning of six years that included many terribly difficult and upsetting times for us. We were thrown into a necessary personal evolution that we had no choice but to undertake. We were in it, and the only way out was down and through it. We had no idea of how deep we needed to go, what the outcome of it all might be, and as we went along, how, or even if, we could stay together and live through the chaos and pain of it all.

Difficult events continued the next day after getting the table. Phil was going shopping for his office desk and chair, and he did not ask me to go with him. I tried, once again, to let it go, and asked him if he wanted me to go with him, knowing how difficult it could be to do so much alone. He said he did not care.

I felt totally dropped, as if I did not exist. Nevertheless, I knew I wanted to go and be together as best we could. It was painful for me, and I am sure for him. And – of all things – we had a bar mitzvah party to go to that night. We went. I sat at a table at the very back feeling horrible pain and aloneness. I stayed in the same spot the whole evening.

The following day, I broke. I started screaming at Phil in anger and rage. I told Phil everything he had done to hurt me, and I did not leave out anything from the past twenty years. I focused especially on the most recent experiences of being disrespected.

I was about to reach the age of seventy, and I resolved I would no longer live without respect. After my outburst of rage and resentment, this resolve remained strong. It was the prelude to what followed – seismic shifts in my deepest attitudes and feelings toward myself and my life.

I came to the sensed realization that my life is my own, and it is my prerogative and right to decide how I am going to live my life. This way of feeling was now my ground. Being almost seventy, I was going to make the decisions about how to live my life. This conviction remains and has continued to deepen and develop.

What We Had to Do

I do not know how long I boiled with anger and resentment, ready to tell Phil all the times he had disrespected me, and wanting him to say, "I'm sorry." Almost every day I had angry outbursts at him, demanding that he say that he was sorry for using the word "imbecilic." That one word encapsulated a lifetime of being disrespected and forever trying to find some way of doing everything exactly right to gain respect and love.

This went on sporadically for two or three months. Gradually I gained some distance on my resentment and anger, and something shifted. I could see Phil's pain and distress and knew that I was also responsible for what had happened. For me, seeing him in pain always had been an almost unbearable experience. This time I did not become frantic. I could let Phil be who he was, even experiencing such distress, and I did not have to get so involved with him.

During this time, I often panicked about losing Phil, but I maintained my resolve. I would no longer accept living with disrespect, nor would I continue forever to embrace guilt and remorse about my behavior, feeling again and again that I had been the cause of everything that was wrong. Sometimes the chaos of my feelings left me feeling nearly psychotic, and I did not have anyone to turn to except Phil. I was alone in a new country, and I had to find my own way. I drew on my own resources, but even amid the turmoil, I had the support of Phil's presence and the knowledge that he did care for me. One way I was able to stay present was to continue taking care of our everyday needs, providing a familiar security for both of us.

Now my priority confronted me clearly. I had to focus on myself and take care of my personal, emotional development. Also, I wanted to take care of our daily life. I knew I could not manage those two priorities and the demands on my energy of clinical work and teaching. I had been working since I was twenty, and now, at seventy, I retired from all professional work.

To further help manage my stress, I walked about three miles and climbed our six flights of stairs each day. I also did daily bioenergetic workouts that relieved stress and helped me with my feelings.

Phil was having an extremely difficult time, and I was pained to see his suffering. Nevertheless, I held on to my conviction that, regardless of the immediate chaos and disaster, I was getting hold of *becoming my own agent for my life*. For me, this was a matter of having my own life or not.

CHAPTER 28

Abuse in Therapy

M

Before writing about being sexually abused by my therapist, "M," I had to weigh my feelings of shame and humiliation. What persuaded me was my understanding that the way I was trapped into his abuse is revealing in relation to my history and my sexual difficulties. Also, I want therapists, and women considering therapy, to be aware of the vulnerability of women who have similar histories to mine. I label that vulnerability "lack of self-agency."

I was thirty-one when I began my first psychotherapy with an analytic psychiatrist. I saw him for two years. I had ideals and convictions about the importance of psychotherapy, so for me just the ritual of going gave me some support. But I needed help in identifying, having, and expressing my feelings; however, he sat and listened and rarely responded, so my therapy did not give me the help I needed. I do not remember how I ended the therapy.

M was my second therapist. From first meeting him, I responded to his way of listening and talking with me. He felt easy to be with, and I felt the contact I had been missing. I regained my hopes and convictions about psychotherapy and again felt willing to invest emotionally and financially. I told him my concern about my numbing, and I was able to relate my family history as I knew it at that time. I talked about my daily life and my ongoing relationship of several years. I felt my therapy was moving along.

I have not forgotten the moment of his first sexual approach. I was lying on the couch talking about events in my life, and I believed he was listening. I looked at him, and I felt grateful for his attention. At that moment, I felt my heart like a child, trusting and nonsexual.

He got up from his chair, came over, grabbed me in his arms and proceeded to kiss me. I struggled, then went numb. I could not speak to express my feelings, and I could not say the one word, "No!"

I had reached a sensitive point in my therapy. I had just opened myself to a first experience of feeling trust and love for a man. The love I felt at that moment was not for him and did not belong to him. He grabbed me to grab the love for himself.

M ignored my numbing and lack of response. He was also oblivious of violating my relationship and how that would harm me and my partner. After coming to know who he was, I can assume that he responded to my loving look out of his desperate need. He was not in contact with his need.

The Sad Trail of Abuse

My memory is sketchy as to what happened after M's assault. I knew I did not want to be sexually or personally involved with him. I did not want to continue the therapy; but at first I did not have sufficient agency for myself, so I did not say an emphatic "NO!" and leave immediately. But it wasn't long before I was able to find the movement to leave.

Confused feelings jumbled inside me, and I could not sort them out. Talking with someone and asking for help did not occur to me. Right after M grabbed me, he quickly got up and locked the door, indicating to me that I was now in a taboo arena with him. Automatically, I kept what happened to myself, as if it were a secret I was bound to keep. As I learned later, this was an indication that I was reliving traumatic experience from my adolescent years.

I do not recall how I left that session or how I felt when I got home. I am sure I was numb, and that I had numbed my upset and heartbreak.

There is a gap in my memory between that occasion and what I next recall. I was attending a workshop given by M. Towards the end of the workshop, we took a break, and I went outside and sat on some steps. M came by.

He said something to the effect of, "Well, have you decided?"

I felt his expectation, and I felt pressured. I must have been responding to his desperation, and I was feeling responsible.

I said, "Yes."

I can remember only two times I was with him with the expectation we would be sexual. There was no sex either time. On the second occasion, I started screaming and then crying. This intense response was my "No." That was the end of that.

This was a confused and strange time for me. I felt trapped, and I felt obliged to be available for a sexual relationship, but where there was no sex and no love. I discontinued therapy with M and started seeing another therapist, a woman. It was some years before I was able to understand that his behavior was abuse, recognize the harm he had caused, and realize how he disrupted my goal of having a relationship with the man of my choice.

M soon started a relationship with another woman. He

wrote me a letter that said he must stop seeing me. This struck me as odd; I had not considered we were "seeing each other." And he wrote the letter in pencil on a scrap of paper that looked like it was torn out of a school tablet. I wadded it up and threw it in the trash. I was left feeling horribly disrespected.

With this tawdry ending to the whole affair, I ended up feeling used and abused. But, again, I still did not have the capability to confront him with his betrayal, disrespect, and abuse. The woman therapist I was seeing did not, or could not, help me. She had experienced something similar with her former male therapist, so her capability was compromised.

I told no one, not even my friend Phil, about what had happened in my therapy.

My continued friendship with Phil was comforting for me during this confusing time. Before he left for a sabbatical year in California, we would have lunches together.

In the Taboo Arena

About a year after the abuse, a group of colleagues, including M and Phil, formed a weekly group to study Reichian therapy. For my work, I felt it was important to be in the group, and this complicated resolving the whole matter. More than three years went by before we revealed our sexual imbroglio to the group. It had been a secret until then. They learned I discontinued my therapy within weeks and that the whole affair ended shortly after it began.

The group did not know what to make of my situation, nor did they know what to do about it except to listen and be with me. I, of course, took responsibility for it happening. "After all," I said, "I am an adult, so I must share the responsibility equally with him." There was a period in the 1990s when many psychiatrists in the country, and especially in our area, were outed for having sexually abused their clients. This behavior had been hidden for years. Now it was seen for what it was: abusive, unethical, and a betrayal of the professional therapist–patient relationship. But this was long after the time of our group.

After our disclosure, I continued with the group, perhaps for a few months. By that time, I had begun therapy with Dr. Lowen, and with his support, to my great relief, I left the group.

Lost Chance

I had held the secret and all the feelings that I was left with for three years. In holding the secret, I numbed my anger, my sadness, and the pain of my distrust. In the years that followed, I learned how destructive this whole episode was for me. The therapeutic development that had started was disrupted and stopped. The effect on me was also destructive of my relationship of many years. I had not developed within that relationship, and it ended.

M betrayed my trust and my love, and he betrayed the ethical grounds of our relationship. The love I had felt in my therapy was an awakening of my possibilities for building a relationship with a man of my choice. M violated those sacred possibilities.

His betrayal returned me to my trauma state where the possibilities for love were again locked away. Now my subsequent therapeutic endeavors would not only be more difficult, they would be nearly impossible – as would be my effort to establish a love relationship.

CHAPTER 29

Light on Hidden Darkness

Psychedelics

In my self-study I have used psychedelic substances – LSD, psilocybin mushrooms, MDMA, and another phenethylamine referred to as 2CB. Phil and I learned how to make use of these substances for the purpose of facilitating our developmental work. MDMA is the only one we have used in the past twenty-five years. We gradually limited our use to two times a year and then only once or none a year. Interestingly, after a time, we did not experience a need to use a substance.

The times I felt intense pleasure with MDMA did not involve my past or my family. The MDMA allowed me to experience the pleasure that was potentially present in my body and my self in my daily life. However, some MDMA experiences felt as if I were being pulled into feelings from the past, and my mind would be drawn into searching within for answers and for clear memories, without knowing exactly what I was looking for. In these experiences, vague memories and fantasies flowed through my awareness, but they did not provide answers. At the same time, the experience itself always has the quality of feeling relevant and important.

Since retiring (not *because* I retired, but in that time frame), I used marijuana two or sometimes three times a month, until recent years when again, I used it less. In my way of using marijuana, I found it particularly helpful for exploring my sexuality generally, and specifically it has allowed me to grasp the reality of my sexual trauma and its effects. It has helped to soften my fear of excitement and of losing control, and it has helped me work with difficult sexual blocking, a key element of my dissociation. A wonderful, surprising effect of MDMA and marijuana was the opening of self-love and how that allowed more capacity for loving Phil.[5]

I will now describe three of my LSD experiences, which were like revelations.

"Phil, I Have a Secret"

Phil and I were on our winter vacation in the Caribbean, where we had rented a little private cottage in a beautiful setting. One day we took LSD.

At one point, I said to Phil, "I have a secret." That was all I could say, "I have a secret."

We went inside and sat at a table, and Phil asked if I could say my secret. I opened my mouth to let out a sound, although I had no idea what I was going to say. After the sound, what came out of my mouth was, "He was psychotic." I knew I was referring to my father. I had no more to say. That was it. That was the secret. What came out of my mouth that day surprised me. That is how these things would just come – without any prior thinking. This experience with LSD began to illuminate my hidden darkness.

---

5 In Chapter 12, "Phil Enters My Life," I describe other positive, pleasurable experiences with psychedelics.

[*Note from Phil*: As Vellie struggled to say her secret, her face underwent a striking metamorphosis. It lost its womanly beauty, and as if mirroring, it became a face I could readily identify as her psychotic father's. The face was old, an ugly fusion of male and female, and psychotic looking, a dark horrible face. It was as if his psychotic face were imprinted on hers.]

Over the years I came to see that behaviors that were a puzzle to me were adaptations to trauma. For many years I doubted and did not want to believe that my father having periods of psychosis were a source of these traumas. Now I am reasonably certain that my statement, "He was psychotic," accurately reflects my experience with him. It shows me who my father was to me, and I am better able to understand myself, my life, and my adaptive behaviors. Phil's observations of me during that moment confirm my revelation.

A Joke

A year or more later I had a terrifying experience while on LSD. I found myself sitting against the head of my bed, my arms up, and horribly terrified. In my mind was the image of my father pointing his gun at me (he owned a handgun that he kept in his desk drawer). In my image, he was laughing, and he pulled the trigger, revealing that the gun was not loaded. It was all a "joke" (my father constantly "teased"). My whole body started to shake. I shook for a long time, while terror went through and left my body.

The Unimaginable Shock

The third LSD experience also had to do with my father. It was the most terrifying of all, an unimaginable shock. These LSD experiences were probably spread over a three- to four-year period.

I was walking around in our house in Pepperell enjoying the psychedelic state. I walked from one room into another. As I walked through the doorway, I was surprised and shocked, and I said, "Mr. J?" At the same time, I felt horrified by what I thought I saw, and I could not say anything else. What I experienced was as if I were seeing something so terrible that my brain was having trouble registering and forming an organized picture. Then, in that split moment, I had the impression of hearing the words, "Kill her." And those words seemed to connect with the reaction of my father and Mr. J to my seeing them in that moment.

Then I began acting strangely. I started crawling around the edges of the room on my hands and knees, feeling terrified, and begging not to be killed. Then there was a blank in my awareness (as if I had either blanked out from the shock or fainted from terror). The next thing I became aware of was that "The Old Woman" (a friend of our father) as we called her, was there doing something to try to bring me to. I do not know what she was doing, something to help me that had a warmth.

What happened next is difficult to describe. All the imagery I had been having during the LSD experience went away, and I felt a kind of blankness. At the same time, I was conscious of what I had just gone through. This peculiar blankness (with memory) felt as if I were experiencing what had happened in the past – that is, the whole episode was somehow put away as if it never existed and so that it was never again to come into awareness; so I would never ever be able to talk about it – except that it did leave a kind of blank space in my awareness.

Historically, about that time, Mr. J disappeared, and we understood that he was in rehab for his alcoholism. The whole family left our neighborhood for a period of time.

Toward the end of my last year in high school, I took on

some odd behavior toward my father. Occasionally I became aggressive and dominant in relation to him. When I recalled this behavior in later years, it puzzled me, because it was so discrepant from other memories of how I had been with him. If we had company, I would tell him that he should get dressed and what he should wear.

I might have threatened him on one occasion. One of my sisters had just become engaged, and she was bringing her fiancé to dinner. My father, in his strange way, was angry. He insisted she return the ring, went to his room, and refused to come to dinner. I went into the room, my parents' bedroom, and closed the door. I vividly remember where he was on his bed. I do not remember what I said, but I do remember how quietly he came to dinner with the family. I have often tried to imagine what I must have said to him.

Once, years later, I saw Mr. J in the hospital where I was working at the time. He was there visiting a family member. He acted very frightened of me, walked by quickly, and did not stop to talk. This was odd. I could not imagine why he avoided me, which is what I felt he did. We had been neighbors for several years and even though it had been a few years in the past, we considered the family as our friends.

Given that even ordinary memories are not, for the most part, historically accurate (as if they were photographs) but change over time, it is unlikely that these images and stories, experienced under the influence of LSD, are historically accurate. But the terror and horror in these LSD experiences were so intense and felt so real that it is possible that I experienced these affects in the context of real experiences in the past. And the images and impressions in the LSD experiences could be derived from my real experience from that time. The images and stories are remarkably specific and detailed. What accounts for such specific, idiosyncratic images all pertaining to my father?

For me, there is something more important than the question of historical validity. Each of these experiences involves my father, no other family member. I have no doubt that they are reflections of my experience of my father. They show me who my father was to me, filling in awareness and understanding that had not been otherwise available.

Torture and Its History

A powerful experience a year or so ago brought light to these LSD events. It confirmed my impression that specific, disturbing events occurred during the high school years when I was trapped in the afternoons taking care of my father.

At four o'clock one morning, I woke up feeling anxious, with a general discomfort in my body. Phil was awake, and I told him, "I might have to get up and go read and distract myself." Phil offered the option of staying in bed and talking with him, even if it was four in the morning. He was awake, and I felt he meant it, so I stayed in bed.

I told Phil, "I don't feel good in my body and my head feels stressed. But I do not know what it is about. No content."

I kept complaining about this general state of feeling bad and not knowing what was going on. I thought it might have to do with my father, because I was working on a chapter about him. I started rubbing and pressing my forehead, then the whole front of my head, rubbing and pressing quite hard.

I began complaining about spending all my time writing and not having any pleasure, no "recess." I felt trapped. I was not free to go outside. I could hear myself in my complaint.

After a while, Phil asked me, "Could you be feeling anxious about our being close? We have been sitting close together, feeling intimate while we worked on your chapters."

I kept breathing and feeling what he said, and then I began to feel fear.

To my surprise, I started saying, "I don't want to be close. I don't want anyone to like me or love me." I repeated these declarations two or three times, and I meant it.

Phil reminded me I told him that on my most recent m&m, images of my father had intruded after I experienced pleasure. Now I was rubbing my head even more vigorously and holding my diaphragm because it hurt.

I became more agitated and flooded with emotion, and then I began feeling I was a bad person. My experience took on the quality of reliving traumas with my father. Now, as I write this, I cannot track the sequence, because my memory carries the confusion from those moments.

Lying in bed talking with Phil, I was having difficulty staying present in my connection with him. I knew he, Phil, was here with me, but I was taken over by strong, torturous affects (body states). I told myself, "They are from the past" (body memories), and I knew they *were* from the past, but I still felt terribly tortured. I have often felt tortured, but this time was intense. My diaphragm hurt, and *the feeling of torture was nearly unbearable.*

I said, "I would not have been able to bear this intense torture as a child."

The feeling of torture became stronger, leading Phil to ask me, "Is this punishment (for having closeness)?"

At first, I did not connect with this, but I was feeling guilt as I rubbed my head. Now I rubbed my whole head more strongly. I was trying to relieve an unbearable tension and feeling of guilt, and now I felt punished.

I told Phil that it felt as if the feeling of torture was the result of my pushing my excitement back into my body, and then it turns against me and feels like torture.

I did exactly that as a twelve- and thirteen-year-old girl. I started having strong genital feelings, and they bothered me. I did not know what they were. I pressed my fists into my genitals as hard as I could to make the feeling stop. Eventually, it did, and the feeling was no longer a "problem."

I did not know then that masturbation was the healthy response to my genital feelings. I had no awareness of that at all. As an adult, I talked with other women about self-pleasure, and I was surprised to hear about how much enjoyment some women had, even as children younger than age ten.

I made the deliberate effort to suppress my genital feelings as early as twelve years old. My father's reaction to the boy driving me home from the ice cream party, and his reaction to my wearing a boy's ring in high school, were two events that reinforced that effort. The time spent trapped in the house taking care of my father when I was in high school doubled down on everything that went before. As a child I managed to numb my genital feelings, my excitement, and later I forgot there was such a feeling as pleasurable excitement.

Now, lying in bed with Phil in the early morning, I wondered out loud why I was rubbing my head.

Phil offered, "In my humble opinion ...." (This is how he likes to talk sometimes for a bit of levity, and he is reminding me he does not want to impose his views.)

"In my humble opinion, you're rubbing your head connects to your effort to suppress your genital feelings."

At first, I fought his words, and I told him they felt harsh and accusatory. My alertness for accusation came quickly on board. I felt hurt, and I do not like some of the common words he uses when he refers to my genitals.

A dramatic sensation cut through me at the same time. I felt as if I were cut right through my belly, through my core, from my diaphragm down to my lower abdomen.

I said, "That's 'your' truth. You do not have empathy for me. I feel left bleeding, bare."

Phil assured me, he really did mean it humbly, he was not trying to impose his truth. But I could not tell what was cutting me – the feeling of a lack of empathy on his part or the accurate meaning of what he was telling me. The words I used – "no empathy, harsh, accusatory" – are words that define the quality of my trauma. I wanted to attribute the source of those feelings to Phil to protect myself from the unbearable feelings of being trapped and tortured. I held on to trusting him, and now and then, I held on to him.

Somewhere in my brain, I knew he was trying to help me with my agitation and torturous feelings. I allowed myself to hold the perception of feeling cut open. It did not feel danger-ous. Phil thought it reflected a positive opening. When armor suddenly opens, it can feel that way.

I cannot recapture the process of quieting down, but I did. Intense, torturous feelings had consumed me for two hours. I became quiet and started to feel a shifting or movement that felt like an integrative process.

We slept for a while.

The next day, I viewed the striking image of my abdomen being cut open as marking a signature event in my develop-ment. The image reflects the danger and fear of ever allowing my sexual feelings to come back alive, but the cut dramatically reveals an opening taking place.

The experience of the torture was horrible – intense and unbearable. I lived and felt it in the moment, and I knew it to be a reliving. It must have originated during the two high school years when I felt trapped after school. In the past, at the first hint of this affect state, I would most likely have screamed, felt crazy, and run away. Now, in that early morning, remaining in bed with Phil's support and understanding, I was able to hold the experience, contain it, and have enough separation to observe and monitor it as I told Phil about it.

A Revelation

This event prepared the way for another signature event just a few days later. I had always managed my need to regulate closeness by keeping a distance between myself and Phil almost all the time. At the same time, I held on to him. Whenever we were getting along nicely and feeling closer, I often found a way to throw a psychological monkey wrench into the works. These were perfectly geared to throw Phil off, get him upset, and distance himself from me.

Such an occasion occurred not so long ago (this was some time after the early morning four o'clock session). I kept apologizing for upsetting him; he kept isolating and acting alone and miserable. Finally, after several invitations to tell me what he was feeling, he did. He insisted I take responsibility for my age-old pattern and change. Later, Phil said he had one more thing he wanted to say. He had what amounted to a revelation for both of us.

Phil told me, "Look! You are not afraid of being close. You are close with me a lot. What happens is that closeness triggers you. You're terrified of being trapped and tortured the way you were with your father!"

Those two words – "trapped" and "tortured" – reached right into me. I began to cry. And I felt the horror of that experience. Then Phil said something else. He said, "This is the memory! This is the memory you have been looking for. It has been there all along. You know what happened to you with your father. You were trapped and tortured." This revealed my motivation for getting out, moving on, staying anonymous. No one was going to trap me and torture me again!

Then I saw something else about the way in which I had been trapped. Even when I managed to keep Phil at a distance, I also managed to keep his attention focused on me to a remarkable degree. I kept him involved with me virtually 24/7. I realized that was my father's way of relating to me! He kept me focused on him and involved with him but without having a real connection with me. He added to the torture of involving me with himself by controlling me, watching me, being involved in my sexuality, and stopping my excitement every time I started to express it in my life.

His preoccupation with my sexual development was not in the service of supporting my becoming a woman. The hurtful effects were reinforced because I felt compelled to be there and take care of his personal needs, food, and clothes. Whether it extended to involving me physically is yet an open question.

CHAPTER 30

My Past Comes with Me

The past is an inheritance, a gift, and a burden.
It cannot be shirked. You carry it everywhere.
There's nothing for it but to get to know it.

– Jill Lepore, *These Truths* (2018)

An M&M Session

One Friday evening prior to an m&m session, I was once again enjoying sharing with Phil my memory of ambling out of the house alone as a five- and six-year-old and following my path to the creek. I was struck by the image of leaving the house unnoticed by the adults. But I was particularly enjoying the memory of the vividly sensuous feelings in my body. I remembered my enjoyment of being alone and feeling free. The feeling was light and full and good, all at the same time.

At the beginning of my m&m session that evening, I relaxed into a sensuous body feeling that reminded me of the way I felt as a child when I ambled barefoot on the path to the creek. After a time, the pleasurable feelings in my body gave way to numb tension, a disappointing but familiar experience. Breathing, grounding, and masturbating did not awaken my feelings. I felt cold and moved close to the heater, then I put on my warmest nightgown and got into bed. I did not recognize my body contraction. Instead, I decided I did not feel any effect from the marijuana. My thought was, "My receptors are not working," but my actions the following day revealed that I had been affected.

Next Day

Phil came in from his walk, and I noted the time and said emphatically, "I worked as fast as I could to get our dinner ready."

I did not pay any attention to what I said and thought I was feeling satisfaction along with a little excitement about getting our meal together. Phil wondered aloud about my saying, "I worked as fast as I could." After several minutes and a few more exchanges about the meal, I felt as if I had been challenged and felt defensive. At that point, my attention jumped to unwrapping a package from a friend containing delicate, old wine glasses. Phil was standing nearby and said, "Be careful," when he noticed I was pulling on the package in a way that could possibly break the glass. He had been responding to my tension all along.

I heard him, slowed down, and began watching myself from the outside, telling myself to be careful. I did not react overtly to Phil's comments, but my mother's voice rang in my ears: "You are a blunderbuss ... So careless." I hated her for making me feel awkward and ugly in my movements, and now I felt the shame and anger that comes into me when I feel I have been called out for tense actions.

When we sat to eat, Phil said something, and it sounded like another comment about me, and I burst out with, "Oh, shut up!"

Then I was afraid I had really "done it."

Phil said he was trying to be friendly, and then I could hear that he was wanting to have contact with me. But I was reliving something, and whatever he would do would not stop it. I had been in my inner world all morning. I became quiet, and I ate slowly.

As we cleaned up the kitchen, I continued at the same slow pace. I became aware I was locked into old negative attacks on myself: *how horrid I am for the outburst*; *shame and humiliation*; *self-hate, along with impulses to harm myself*. I was in a fit of shame, and I was in a rage that turned on myself. I became exhausted from my intense feelings, from seeing how I affected Phil, and from the fear that my rage had once again pushed him away.

However, he stayed with me and asked what made me say, "I worked as fast as I could." I did not have an answer other than what I had first said, that I was feeling satisfaction and excitement. But now that did not feel quite right, and I said, "I do not know."

He said, "working as fast as I could" did not feel to him as if it fit in with who we are together. I was tense and edgy, but I was listening and bringing myself to focus on my immediate contact with Phil and being with him. Our contact and talking together brought me back to what I experienced the evening before, the shift from pleasurable sensuous feelings to feeling numb and becoming cold.

Later in the afternoon, I started experiencing a state of terror. I began having images of how I felt when I would come into the house after school, during the time I was given the responsibility of helping my father get ready for work.

The images involved details of the house that I had not recalled in sixty-five years. I could see each piece of furniture and where it was located, the colors of everything, the tiles on the kitchen floor, and even the water kettle on the stove.

The intense terror continued during the evening, so Phil suggested I get in bed where I would feel safe. Phil's empathy and the warmth in bed gave me the sense of security I needed to go to sleep.

Terror

Next morning, I recalled the terror. I tracked what had happened starting the evening before the m&m and remembered the talk about ambling out of the house as a young child. My ambling out of the house had been a spontaneous movement to get away from the family environment. I was drawn to being alone in nature where I felt free and good. As I felt my terror, again I had images of how I felt as an adolescent when my responsibilities for my father trapped me in the house, and I could not follow my wish to be outside and free.

The difficult feelings of fear and terror that began the day after the m&m continued. The terror was the worst; it was different from fear. It made me tremble inside, and at times my eyes became alert and watchful. I made movements to soothe my arms and would find myself wringing my hands.

One day that same week, I was waiting at the eye clinic. I went to the bathroom, and for a few minutes I was in an empty, quiet space. In those minutes, alone in the quiet space, I sensed in my being what I knew about the terror. The terror had been from having experienced a physical threat.

Twice under the influence of LSD I experienced terror (see Chapter 29, "Light on Hidden Darkness"). Both times carried the feeling of reliving actual experiences with my father. Both were specific and detailed scenes in which I was physically threatened, and the experience and terror felt real. I have no memory of ever having had such experiences with my father. For me to invent two scenes that are so specific, detailed, and terrifying is not impossible. However, neither is it impossible that both scenes carry representations of historical realities where I did experience terror. At a minimum, I take these LSD experiences as strong indications that I experienced terror in situations with my father in real life.

In addition, on my first LSD experience involving my father, I said, "I have a secret. He was psychotic." And at the time, Phil saw the dramatic shift of my facial appearance to someone who looked as if she were seeing and mirroring a crazed person. I knew that my father was the object of my secret and the mirrored expression. I did not experience terror on that occasion, but I was revealing my father to be someone who could very well have terrorized me at times.

The experiences of terror I have described are givens. How my behavior changed during my last high school years is also a given. Experiencing terror – and horror – during that time could account for the changes in my personality, the way I acted around my peers, especially male peers, and the changes in my appearance and typical manner of holding my body. They were not on the scale of "normal" behavior changes of an adolescent.

Why Then?

In the m&m, my experience shifted from feeling good in my body to coldness and loss of feeling. Something akin to fear accounts for that shift, arising in response to feeling good. I was not aware of being frightened then or the next day when my anomalous reactions to Phil caught his attention. But he was affected and followed up with his inquiries.

I did not want my fear and anger brought to my attention, and I reacted to him with defensive anger. Feeling my anger frightened me, and later I felt terror and went to bed for safety. I had been trying to avoid the terror all along. I lived with the terror for a few days, identified my body states, and made the association with my father. It was more difficult to feel the rage that had opened and my fear of how I expressed the rage toward Phil.

This whole sequence, leading to my experience of terror, had been set in motion by a disturbing experience three weeks earlier. On that occasion too, I was preparing for an m&m. As an experiment, I initiated this session by eating a brownie I made with cannabis-infused butter. To my surprise, I began to have strong erotic feelings. In my excitement, I impulsively ate two more brownies.

The pleasure and excitement shifted to contraction. My diaphragm muscles spasmed painfully, and I became cold. I started to get in bed, but when I moved, I became nauseous. For the next two to three hours I was on the floor, in pain, throwing up and retching, while Phil watched over me with concern. My diaphragm muscles were involved so intensely I was quite uncomfortable for a couple of days after.

Even at the time, I was able to reassure Phil. I knew from experience that my pain and nausea were caused by the release of chronic contractions, long held, deep tensions in and around my diaphragmatic muscles. Shocking experience and terror would cause this kind of contraction. It is as if the tissue freezes.

Under the influence of the marijuana, the chronic tensions began to let go, and those muscles began to spasm, causing the pain and nausea. In the days following my "brownie experience," we had many talks about the terror and its sources.

On my m&m three weeks later, I contracted intensely against my pleasurable feelings. While I did not feel terror during those contractions, I did experience it in the days immediately following. This chain of experiences was an integrative process. The significance of it was that I could now identify the body state of terror as separate from a present-moment contact with Phil. And the great benefit of that is that it allows for the possibility of being able to open to feelings of excitement that belong to the present moment. I feel safe with Phil, and I can be more relaxed and happier being together with him.

CHAPTER 31

Back and Forth

Selfology

This chapter describes other work on my relationship with my father, and it illustrates how daily life provides crucial experiences to work with and how we went about it. We like to call this work "self-study," and at some point, we took to calling it "selfology," because that is what it is: the study of the self. Me, as a person, my development, and how I function is the focus of my self-study. We acknowledge that our agency resides in the self, which means that I, as a person, take action or withhold it, and I, myself, claim my life as my own and make my place in the world. It also means that I, myself, am responsible for my taking action to develop and change to relieve pain and find pleasure, joy, and love.

"Back and forth" refers to an aspect of our collaboration. Of course, we share our experiences, our memories, our awareness of ourselves and of each other. We developed the emotional strength to allow the other to give back impressions, understanding, and interpretations that would help our development within our self-study. There is another – and the most interesting – quality to this give-and-take that I shall illustrate and describe later.

As to my work with myself, I have described the state of shock (dissociation) that pervaded my body, blocked feelings of anger and inhibited joy, excitement, sexual pleasure, and the capacity to love. Dissociation also caused a disturbance in my cognitive ability. These states were the most disturbing aspects of my experience throughout my adult life, and they motivated my continuous efforts to free inhibited feelings and sexual pleasure, and find safety, peace, and love.

My work with myself begins and ends with the exploration of here-and-now experience that is grounded in my body. For me, the basic first step in this process was developing the capacity to pay attention in the present moment to my own bodily experience. Disbelief and familiar shaming voices of denial shadowed many years of difficult explorations of my early relationships within my family, especially memories of my father. I was left with haunting feelings of ambiguity and confusion and a yearning for closure. The great advantage of starting and ending with bodily experience is that it cuts through ambiguity and confusion. I pay attention to what is.

Pancake Night

One evening during a visit from a good friend, I served pancakes for supper. Just at the moment I was about to serve them, Phil came into the kitchen and interfered with my plan. He declared how he would do it.

Immediately, I felt sharp anger. I took two pancakes in my hand, pushed the plate away from me, walked over to my place at the table and dropped them onto my plate. As I sat down, I saw that my anger sent Phil into a state of shock. I started having all kinds of terrible feelings. I felt horrified by my effect on him, and I was frightened that I had set off a painful disaster.

"Painful disaster" sounds like extreme language for my life with Phil. But because of a long history of fear of my anger, I did not experience it for many years. Instead of feeling and expressing anger, my outlet was crying and various forms of self-punishment. Now I am capable of experiencing anger, but when I express it toward someone, I can become frightened and frantic, especially if I am already stressed.

Later in the pancake evening when we were alone, I started talking about my feelings. It all boiled down to a familiar litany, "I am a failure; I never really learned how to cook and cannot cook; and cooking always creates stress."

Often cooking has felt like torture, and for many years, I blocked out of my thinking the whole idea of preparing and serving food. There were times when I did not cook even when I invited someone for a meal. I would be oblivious to the need to prepare food, which created some socially awkward moments.

The next day, after pancake night, I took time to pay attention to myself. As I was talking my voice sounded noticeably young. I had switched to being the child in my family. I was no longer Vellie, the person I am now, and I was no longer able to ignore my pain. I recognized a familiar body state of horror. I never found a memory to explain this pain and horror. I have found clues that take me back to the time when I was responsible for preparing my father's food before he left for work. I have searched for clear memories of what kind of abuse might have had such effects on me, and I have not found any. I learned that memories cannot be "found" by searching for hidden ones, as if finding memories were like going through stuff left in the attic.

Phil Internalizes and Returns It
(Back and Forth)

We continued our dialogue the following day. I learned that Phil
had awakened during the night, and he got up and sat quietly
in our great room in his rocker. He told me his mind had been
working with what he had taken in from my talking. He said
he simply could not figure out or understand what the whole
pancake episode was all about. Usually if he lets his mind focus,
he will come to a good and useful understanding. This time, no.

Then he continued. He said we could take a "bold leap,"
as he put it. He believed we could relate the upset and terrible
feelings I had been having the past two days to my experience
with my father in my last two years in high school. From this
talk, I realized *I do know. I know a lot about what happened to
me.* My habitual, "I don't know," is simply not true.

I know what was happening in my father's life during the
time I was in high school and responsible for taking care of him
after school. He was working long hours as a night watchman
at a toxic chemical plant. He was attempting to sleep during hot
humid Louisiana days with no air conditioning. He was alone
all week without any contact with anyone other than myself.
His father, who was bedridden from a stroke, died during this
time. My father was in his fifties, an age when he should have
had a work life with some satisfaction or fulfillment, but he
did not. Now, his wife was staying away from him and was not
taking care of his daily needs. His childhood left him severely
undeveloped as a person with the capacity to function in the
world. All of this left him alone, desperate, and with uncon-
trollable states of rage that I now label as psychotic episodes.

Phil was awake again the following night. The next morning, he talked with me about a realization he had during the

night that was very distressing to him. He envisioned me living day in, day out, for all the weeks of each school year, having to be alone in the afternoons with a disturbed father who did not see me for myself and was incapable of being there for me as a positive paternal influence. Phil felt how oppressive, stultifying, frightening, and sometimes horrifying that must have been for me.

Phil told me it dawned on him that his empathic feeling for me came so alive because of his own similar experience. He lived year in, year out, under the oppressive shadow of his much older brother. He told me that when this came to mind, he found himself shaking involuntarily. He said he shook for several minutes.

Another Back-and-Forth

Another back-and-forth a few weeks after pancake night took me a step further. It was another occasion when I snapped at Phil. This time, I did not get into terrible feelings and neither did Phil. But he again internalized something, and the next day he was angry, and he had a lot to say. A profound realization resulted for both of us.

He told me that it dawned on him that I had been "conned." I had been conned by my father, and by my mother as well, into unquestioning obedience to be home every day after school "to get my father off to work." (I had repeatedly used that phrase, without being aware of its ambiguity, having in mind only that it meant "getting him off to work.") I gave up my teenage after-school social life to take care of him. I had been conned into believing it was an unquestionable necessity.

Phil was angry. He said he had been conned too. The idea that it was necessary for me to be home after school to take care of my father was all utter nonsense. I had been manipu-

lated and conned into relinquishing my life, and now I was still
struggling to get it back, and Phil had been struggling along
with me to understand and support me – all over a big lie, a
bunch of rubbish. My father could have taken care of himself.
Neither my father nor my mother had enough feeling for me
to allow me to have my own life. Instead, I had to take care of
an unhappy, disturbed man who was my father.

How Things Go Back and Forth

I have always listened when Phil comes back to me with his
feelings and understanding of something I have been expressing. When he talks about something on his mind, and I respond
with my understanding, he listens to me. It is as if our inner
worlds exchange messages back and forth in a way that we are
not aware of.

Phil calls what I do my "fingy," meaning that seemingly
out of the blue I have "put my finger on" the crux of some issue
he has been discussing with me. A similar process happens with
Phil. He experiences a process in his mind, his feelings, and
his body. It goes along on its own, often during the night, and
significant insights emerge. This is how minds work; or more
exactly, this is how two selves work when they are emotionally
engaged.

PART VIII

Phil

The road to liberation from the traumatized self is therefore frequently rocky and can feel treacherous … yet through a therapeutic alliance that provides safety, perseverance, and ongoing instillation of hope, the traumatized self can slowly learn to break free from its imprisoned state, attaining a life that is less constrained by … pain and torment.

– Paul Frewen and Ruth Lanius, *Healing the Traumatized Self* (2015)

CHAPTER 32

An Underground Sexual Self

A second significant psychoanalytic discovery is that the
individual develops not by abolishing the archaic mind, but
by incorporating it into the structure of the individual soul.

– Jonathan Lear, *Love and Its Place in Nature* (1960)

A Different Kind of Hero

I have a memory of a body state, which I would now call
erotic, from when I was eleven or twelve. In this memory, I
am alone, and I am standing at the south edge of the front
porch of my family home looking down at the ground, a drop
of a few feet. In front of me is our imposing Norwegian blue
spruce, a protective sentinel rising to my second-story bedroom
window. Within myself I am cultivating a vaguely erotic fantasy
accompanied by a familiar lonely, longing quality. I imagine
myself lying on the ground, just below where I am standing,
curled on my side, sheltering under the boughs of my tree. I
am grievously wounded, shot by "the enemy," a casualty of

brave self-sacrifice to save my friends in the war. Hopefully, I will be found, and my heroism and sacrifice appreciated. I contemplate letting myself fall off the edge of the porch, but I back away from the possibility of real injury. The feeling runs through my body, mildly erotic, achy, with a sense of passive dissolution of my form. The immediate context for my reverie was a war game I played with the boys next door.

I call this constellation of feelings, images, and fantasies my *chthonic sexual persona*. I like the word "chthonic." It means "of the earth, but below the surface of the earth." "Persona" suggests that there is an alternative personality to the one on the surface, and it suggests that both personalities have a kind of fluidity. Neither is totally solid and defined, and they can flow, one to the other.

I understand my chthonic sexual persona as a distinct, erotic part of me that remained hidden underground. Humiliation and submission shaped this erotic development. The mix of passivity and self-derogation masked by fantasies of self-sacrifice feels shameful. I kept this sexual persona hidden, but I did long to be "found."

The Fire Setter

Another memory associated with the same porch stands in bright contrast with my chthonic persona. The brick steps going up to the porch from the sidewalk formed a nook where the steps meet the porch at a right angle. Evergreen bushes filled this nook, and when I crawled in among them, I had a secret hideaway. Here, at a younger age, I anxiously built tiny fires of little dry sticks, arranged with care and precision. I sneaked matches from the kitchen, and when I lit the fire, small flames quickly licked up around the twigs, and the fire burned beautifully.

Once they were going, I became frightened about being caught. One day, after building a fire that very morning, I was in kindergarten (as my memory has it). Sandy, a cute little girl, lying on the floor, playfully grabbed my ankle and pulled me towards her. I became frightened she would smell the fire on my clothes. I tried to pull away. This memory dates my fire setting to five years old.

The older boy, with his fantasy of martyred injury and hope of being found, lost the liveliness of the little fire setter, although the latter's excitement was laced with fear of discovery. My fire making as a little boy seems to me like a last-ditch effort at retaining my excitement and aggression, just before they were doused and smothered by domination, fear of injury, and prohibition.

The fire setter, however, was not entirely extinguished. One day, as an older boy, after the war games, I showed off my skills with stolen matches to two other boys. This time I set our back field ablaze, precipitating a visit from the town Volunteer Fire Department. (I was awed to see the big fire trucks right there in our field.)

And as a teenager, experimenting with homemade gun powder, I came close to blowing myself up and burning the house down. Luck intervened because my mixture burnt slowly with a lot of smoke but did not blow up.

Living a Myth

In the years Vellie and I have been together, suffering took me over time and again. I seemed to have a gift for it. I would feel grievously injured, unappreciated, abused, and hurt; the unhappy victim, long suffering, made more sympathetic by martyrdom and self-sacrifice. I lingered in this state for lengths of time. I could hardly avoid asking myself, "Why all this suffering?"

The seed for this condition was germinating in me as I stood on the front porch nurturing into subliminal awareness my chthonic sexual persona. By the time I was with Vellie, my suffering was a fixation and "emitted" an array of messages: real pain, hate, revenge, punishment of myself, as well as the other, a cry to be found and helped, and the vague aroma of perverted sexuality. The messages told the other person:

> I am a victim of your abuse; I accuse you; look what you have done to me; you have left me; you have betrayed me; abase yourself and come back and save me; I am showing you how you deserve to suffer; I will make you suffer as I do, and more of the same.

My chthonic persona was a private myth that I lived out in my frequent episodes of suffering. I asked Vellie if she recognized me in this description.

She does.

Had she experienced me this way?

Yes; of course, a lot.

Indeed, during the difficult Hapardess years, this state dominated my life on and off for months on end. Vellie was with me as I endured repeated cycles of descent into the chthonic depths. Had she not been with me, I do not know if I could have endured it or if I would have grown out of it. I am thankful that the time came when the mythic mists faded, and the sufferer exited the stage.

CHAPTER 33

Father, Brother, Underground Self, Panic

Why So Angry?

When I felt "hurt," my initial reaction was usually anger. Sometimes I was angry for no obvious reason at all. My voice would get loud; I would yell. Typically, I experienced my anger as natural, appropriate, and justified. Therefore, there was no need to question it. Fortunately, Vellie insisted on questioning it. I was reluctant to change; eventually I knew I had to.

I experienced my angry actions as being driven by an unbearable bodily state. It filled my abdomen, flowed up into my diaphragm, and surrounded and pinched my heart. It was an awful experience. But what made my anger seem so "natural" to me were hidden assumptions or beliefs that felt incontestable. I told myself what I experienced in my body was too much to bear, and I should not have to bear it. Further, it was due to some action of Vellie's.

If you were the way you should be, you wouldn't
do things to make me suffer. If you were right, I
would be saved from having to bear my pain and
suffering. Now that we are together, I should not
have to suffer this way. If I do, it must be because
of you, one way or another.

I hid all such childish and outlandish claims, even from
myself. But my actions attested to them. My anger was another
side of my underground (or, as I prefer, chthonic) persona. The
same pain was woven into both.

Selfscape with Lightning

One day, a few years after the moment on the porch when I
first glimpsed my chthonic persona, I experienced terror. I put
my age at thirteen or fourteen. I was outside in the yard. It
began to rain, and there was lightning nearby. I ran into the
garage, a separate building, about fifty feet from the back door
of the house. Just at that moment, lightning struck close by,
and there was a terrific crack of thunder. Terror overcame me,
as if, at the next moment, God would strike me with lightning.
Panicking, I ran for the house. Once inside, I calmed down, but
I was stunned and confused by the terror.

I did not believe in God, so I had no way to explain my
terror to myself. A few years later, as I was finishing high
school, I found myself pondering, "Does God exist?"

I was seriously preoccupied with this question when I started
college. I read Dostoevsky, took a course on the philosophy of religion, and, for a few weeks, tried to interest myself in reading the
Bible. Halfheartedly, I kept an eye out for a "religious experience,"
but I knew I was not inclined that way. One night my searching
and preoccupation came to a head. Vividly, I see the desk I sat at

and my notebook, as I passionately wrote my conclusion in large script. "God does not exist," and therefore, I am "alone in the universe." I was on my own to establish meaning and safety. After that, the emotional charge around the whole issue dissipated.

Now imagine this: sixteen years later I completed my dissertation for a PhD in clinical psychology titled *The Psychology of Religious Doubt.*

Even before pondering the existence of God the Father and Judge, I was a doubter as a general approach to life. My father's lack of expression and his occasional rage left me susceptible to fear and terror. I had been uncertain about being safe and having a place in my father's house. I had no basis for knowing where I stood in his eyes.

Boy on the Cellar Stairs

With my brother, I had experienced fear even earlier, when I was four or five; he would have been fourteen or fifteen:

I am sitting on the stairway that goes down to the cellar. My brother is down there doing something, so I suppose I have followed him. He is scolding and threatening me. I seize up inside with a horrible feeling, awful. Now I would describe it as a feeling of castration. He is saying things to me, but I never knew what. I am fearful; he is so very angry. He is threatening, and he is so much bigger. I did not know what he might do to me, but for me the situation was at that point – where he might do something to me, something awfully painful, and I am frightened. I contract, squeezing in my outrage; I am helpless. I do not know if, even then, I knew what it was all about. I do not remember any resolution, other than being left with that awful feeling in my body.

I never made much of this memory. After all, whenever I spoke about my family, I would invariably say, "My brother was the one person in the family I could love." Seemingly, I set aside this memory of humiliation and fear to preserve the love story, thus resolving the dissonance.

But now I have questions, and they carry outrage.

Who did my brother think he was, frightening, domineering, and humiliating me? What gave him the right?

I looked to my brother as a second father. My heart failed me at the prospect of facing his much greater size and power in an angry confrontation. My voice carried little weight in the family in any case.

And why was I – to the degree suggested by this memory – so under his thumb for my "education?" And how come the education was so threatening?

I do not recall anyone else treating me that way.

Where was my father? Or mother? Had I been turned over to him?

Other questions are even more disconcerting because they have implications for how I am now.

How in the world did I go from being this shrinking, frightened little kid to the adoring little brother? How do those two fit with each other?

What accounts for this dissonance and what happened to the anger and rebellion that would inevitably be engendered – at some point – by that kind of tyranny? What happened to my aggression?

These last questions are doubly disconcerting because the dissonance itself reveals what happened. I adapted to a physical threat by setting aside fear and hate and orienting myself towards my brother with passivity and idealization – supposedly, "love" – to elicit his love and protection. The aggression that might have fueled my capacity to disentangle myself from my brother was perverted into submissiveness and woven into my chthonic sexual persona.

Boy on His Dad's Lap

As a small boy, I had the "privilege" (and I thought of it as such), as the youngest child, of going to my father after we had finished eating our evening meal and requesting to sit on his lap. I liked to play with his bushy eyebrows. He would remove his glasses and submit to this petting without protest or pushing me away. Remembering myself in that situation leaves me feeling a little queasy.

I wanted to believe I had a special relationship with Dad, the head of the family; special as compared with my brother and sister, maybe even my mother, who in my eyes, was not much fun. However, I did not feel secure in such a belief. I was afraid of my father. He could blow up.

One evening I ran through the house with him in hot pursuit. I escaped by running into the downstairs bathroom, slamming and locking the door, and going out through the window. I was scared. I was running. And make no mistake, that escape route had been plotted out long before that evening. I was ready to execute. My planning rested on an underlying uneasiness and vigilance.

It seems to me, that as long as I was a boy – before adolescence (and masturbation) – I could be a pet for my father, at least most of the time. As an adolescent, I was no longer a pet, and I had no indication that he took any pleasure or interest in me. I was already in the transition to adolescence the day when lightning struck terror in my heart. As I came into adolescence, I became even quieter and kept to myself; I stayed on the edges and kept my distance. In my father's house, I was not safe enough, nor did I have the support, to develop freely into a full-fledged male self, out in the open.

My father did not openly criticize or demand that I measure up in some way. He did not offer praise, support, or encouragement either. His ways left me uncertain of my standing in his eyes, even questioning if I had any standing one way or another.

When I was that age, he occasionally would drop the phrase, "lazy adolescents." He did not direct it at me, but I had to wonder if I was one of those lazy ones. I did like to sleep in on Saturday and Sunday mornings. Once I began college, work became the center of my life and the focus of the greater part of my energies. Later, I would tell myself that I worked harder and longer than he did.

I remained quietly subservient with older men and teachers. At college, I was desperate to produce work of high enough quality to win the patronage of my advisers. And I did not build confidence in my own capacities.

I acquired another detrimental belief. I grew up under the illusion that my father and brother protected me, and that I – a small, weak person – needed their protection. In my experience of myself I stayed small and weak, so I felt I needed protection in the wider world outside our home.

This whole set of attitudes was an illusion. In my relationships with my brother and father I was frightened and did not feel safe. I could not freely be myself with them, so I dissembled by looking up to them and acting as if I needed their protection.

The fact is, I was on my own – and alone – in the world, taking care of myself from early on. Our father provided a home, a shelter I knew would always be available to me in a time of need. I was grateful for this security, but the "protection" of my illusion is another matter altogether.

Panic

My experiences with my father and brother led to the development of my chthonic sexual persona, leaving me vulnerable when I left home to begin life in the wider world. Unexpectedly, a few years ago that vulnerability appeared one day in full-blown form as panic.

At the conclusion of a talk with Vellie, I told her I was helped by holding to our goals of being able to live together in peace, love, and harmony.

Vellie said, "We wanted to be sexual, to ground our development in our sexuality; if I could do that, I'd be peaceful (chuckles)."

And here, suddenly, I became nervous. *What's happening?* went through my mind. I mumbled something about our m&ms and masturbating.

Vellie picked right up on this theme by reminding me, "Our m&ms are to free our sexual feelings."

Our conversation ended, and I went to my study feeling increasingly frightened in a strange way. I sat and attempted to calm myself by breathing, but my fear became more intense.

A moment later, Vellie knocked and came in to share a thought. "Of course we masturbate; that's learning to love your sexual feelings. That was the motivation that started the whole thing for you. You wanted to heal the cancer, but more deeply, you knew you needed to love your sexual feelings."

What she said was supportive and touched the depth of the matter, but my reaction continued. This was different from fear. I was in a panic, something I had never experienced. My head filled up in an odd way, not quite as if it would explode, but going in that direction. My body had a strange kind of energy going through it. And in my core, I felt as if the content and substance of my self had been blown away in a kind of white-out explosion. Over the course of the day, the panic calmed.

A Lived Injury

When the panic began as I spoke with Vellie, I recalled the feeling of being genitally attacked when we lived on Hapardess. I remembered the panic of the lightning strike. I remembered the fear and awful body state when I sat on the cellar steps trapped in my brother's anger and threats. My chthonic sexual persona was unraveling, opening the path for the male sexual self that had been interrupted as a child. I felt the panic that had been frozen in my body.

CHAPTER 34

Out of the Shadows

Another Night on Happy Meadows

I had given up on sleep and was sitting in the dimly lit kitchen. Memories stirred up by the chapter I worked on during the day insistently came to mind. And out of them a disturbing question persistently called for attention. My memories went back to our time of crisis on Hapardess. They showed me that I had allowed dark elements of my experience to remain shadowed in the periphery of my awareness, making me question myself.

What did I experience – feelings, thoughts, reactions – when I was confronted by the profound changes Vellie was making and by her standing on new ground in relation to me?

I knew the answer. And I knew what I had left in the shadows.

The Unspoken

Shame and fear are reasons to linger in the shadows. So is wanting to keep secrets.

Vellie had set herself and her life on new ground. She had claimed herself as a person in her own right and for herself.

Being together meant I had no choice but to set my own life on new ground. Our relationship and our life together were going to be different.

The implications stood out immediately, like a full-page headline: No more diving into endless, boundless emotional storms; no more "episodes" of pain and despair; no more anger and rage; no more punishing by cold withdrawal; no more silent, mournful accusation; and no more hours and days of suffering on my part, or on hers.

In the beginning, I did not know if I was capable of making such changes. Vellie's changes made it much less likely that she would stimulate or get involved with an episode, which made my task more manageable. Over time, I was able to acknowledge that, yes, at this point in my life, it was possible for me to make the necessary changes, to let go of the storm of painful emotion I was so used to. I felt relief. And I felt a big loss. That was hard to admit. Not having the storm felt like a loss.

But this was not the worst I had to admit to. That night sitting in the kitchen, my heart sank. I had to admit that I had wanted the pain and suffering. And I wanted to hurt back. There it was: the shameful acknowledgment that I sought the excitation and perverse pleasures of my wish to hurt and of my own suffering. I had perpetrated this on Vellie.

In my hurt, I did experience pain, and it could be gut-wrenching and agonizing; I felt it through my abdomen. I experienced it as if the woman were actively *doing something* to me; whether deliberately or not, she was doing it. She was rejecting, or unavailable, or even torturing me by arousing me and then withdrawing and seeming to have no more interest in me than to see me suffer.

Such experiences were common in my intimate life with women. Could I establish a relationship without such experiences and what would it be like for me? In the first place, it would mean relinquishing the belief that all my agony and suffering was caused in some way by the woman.

And Then?

Now, if I stay with Vellie on these new terms, who would I be?

What will it be like not to have familiar outlets? Will all that turbulence sit inside me, like some awful overgrown toad?

My raging was an attempt to relieve myself of the tensions of pain and humiliation. Making her hurt was retribution – she should be made to feel what I had to endure. That gave me relief – or was it satisfaction?

I had lived as if I believed that misery, fighting, perverse satisfaction and excitation wove the connection between myself and her. Without that whole awful state would there still be a connection?

I did not know, but taking counsel with myself, I saw that not knowing indicated that I was on new ground. This opened possibilities of new ways of being. Most importantly, I trusted myself and Vellie to find positive ground based on love and the pleasure of being together. Over the next few years, this is what happened.

Repetition and Punishment

In the kitchen this night, I peered into the shadows. I reminded myself that up to those days on Hapardess, I had been struggling to claim my life as a sexual male. That is what those repetitive storms were all about. But up until then, I went about that struggle by desperately seeking permission and healing – from my mother, from *the woman* – to claim my penis, my genital experience, my whole sexual body, and my right to fulfill my sexual nature. This left me living in the frightened, dependent, guilty position of the humiliated supplicant.

Now I was left with the realization that my experience with my mother conditioned me to understand with certainty that the woman was going to torture, deny permission, and attack. Fighting back and avoiding commitment were based on the desperate denial of my fear, dependence, need for permission, guilt, and humiliation. It was a relentless effort to make a bad outcome better and the refusal to accept that my most natural movement was violated to such an extent that fulfilling it in a natural manner was entangled in difficulties.

Fighting back perpetuated the pain. I protected myself by pushing away the one I wanted to love. Then I was caught in grief and aloneness, just as I was originally. This mix functioned as punishment. I kept arranging the punishment that, as a child, I believed I deserved.

Energy and Eros

In a high degree of excitation, each of us had expended an enormous amount of energy as we lived through stormy episodes. Excitation, love, and eros were at the heart of all our experiences. I had been expressing these vital energies in my life with Vellie in the only way I knew. As emotionally fraught as our situation was when we were on Hapardess, and for years before as well, the wish to love and be loved was the ultimate motivation. Given my circumstances, I was fortunate to be able to claim as much of myself and my life as I did. I was aided by dogged determination and, later in my life, by the good fortune of being with Vellie.

Over these last ten years the whole rumpus dissipated. The excitement of sexual love is not like the excitement of the kind of fixation I was left in. The energy of love is soft and pleasurable; pleasure itself is easy, and enjoyable.

PART IX

Phil

CHAPTER 35

The Broken Bough

Rock-a-bye baby, on the treetops,
When the wind blows, the cradle will rock,
When the bough breaks, the cradle will fall,
And down will come baby, cradle and all.

– Eighteenth-century nursery rhyme

Lullaby

The faintest whisper of long-ago memory tells me my mother sang this lullaby to me. Off and on, I find myself singing it, often as a parody so as to avoid the sad feelings it arouses. I also like to imagine a mother singing to her baby in arms in the way I would imagine would give baby most excitement and pleasure:

[The mother holds her infant in her arms and rocks him as she sings.]

Rock-a-bye baby, [Rhythmic, pleasurable rocking.]

On the treetops, [Baby held close, on her breasts.]

When the wind blows, [A stronger movement, excites baby.]

the cradle will rock, [Exciting, different rhythms.]

When the bough breaks, the cradle will fall, [Movement almost stops; the mother looks just concerned enough to catch baby's attention.]

And down will come baby, cradle and all. [The most exciting movement. The mother bends quickly, giving baby the feeling of falling, even as she cradles him to her breasts. Baby at first is slightly startled, and then bursts into gales of laughter as he feels securely, warmly held, and sees his mother's smile.]

But what happens if the bough breaks and mother is not cradling?

I am climbing on a huge, unending structure, like the girders holding up a bridge. I am terrified, because I cannot hold on, and I'm going to fall, a terrifying fall into nothing. As my grip loosens ... I try desperately to wake up.

As a small boy, that nightmare visited me from time to time. Frantically, I tried to waken myself. Once awake, I might quickly pad into my parents' room and get into bed next to my father. He stirred but did not waken, and feeling safe, I went to sleep.

The Mother Is Missing

One day in a therapy session, I realized I never talked about my mother, and I said, "Listening to me you wouldn't know I had a mother." When I talked about myself with Vellie years later, I would say, "I dropped her."

I do not have fond memories of time spent with her, and I do not remember ever missing her. I recall her presence. I knew her as "Mom," the one who devoted herself to taking care of our meals, clothes, and the house.

I have a tender memory from when I was a small boy:

> We are in the dining room of our house. I am looking at my mother. I think to myself, "When I grow up, I would like to marry someone like her and have her around."

> I walked the four blocks to school and back twice a day from grade school on. When I left in the mornings, my mother would be upstairs. I would call up, "Bye, Mom."

> She would call down, "Be careful."

Besides the evening meal she always prepared for my father's return from work, she anxiously saw to it that I had a meal at lunchtime. She was concerned because I was not much of an eater. I walked home and back for lunch. Most days, Mom would be there. She often fortified a slim bologna sandwich with a raw-egg milkshake. I ate in silence and went back to school.

I appreciated her sense of beauty, color, texture, and arrangement – for house furnishings, clothing, flowers, prints, and pictures.

Talking with Mom

In my teen years, I was remote and uncommunicative with my mother. Occasionally, she would say something to me or ask me something that showed she was aware of me and maybe concerned. One day, she called out from their bedroom asking me to come to her. She was reclining on her chaise longue darning wool socks, a regular task she performed with meditative quietness.

"You never talk to us," she said. "The big kids talked to us."

What she said was true, and I took it as a reproach. But I did not know why she would expect me to talk. On this occasion, she began speaking, and I remained standing awkwardly facing her. I listened without saying anything, and I became aware that even as she was talking to me, I could not for the life of me remember what she was telling me. As compensation I thought, "When I grow up, I will write about her." Remarkably, now I am doing just that.

Separating Emily from Vellie

I lost track of my mother emotionally – who she was to me, how I felt with her, and anything about a relationship between us. A series of experiences over the past few years brought meaning and content to this mother-space that had been largely blank. This is the first: Vellie and I were chatting. As I listened to her, I noticed a familiar tension in my body. It was undefined, slightly disagreeable. I recognized it as the feeling that could intrude and distract me from feeling good with Vellie. I had learned to push it aside. This time, I paid attention. What I felt was distinctly "motherish," something I had never recognized. It felt like a typical daily way I had experienced my mother. My remembered mother became a bit more real to me, and my enjoyment of Vellie was saved from being degraded by this unpleasant feeling.

A Moment of Seeing

The memory of my mother gained further depth with another experience. An occasion when Vellie had been experiencing difficult emotions for a few days evoked a typical anxiety in me: I would be left deprived and alone.

One of those days as we were talking, my self-centered concerns dropped away. I grasped that Vellie was putting her heart and soul into freeing herself from the disastrous effects of her early life traumas. I felt her dedication, her love, her goodness, and her bravery in facing all she had faced. I was humbled and moved; my heart opened, and I felt gratitude and admiration. It was a moment of grace. We both were freed, and there was a new spirit between us.

"I Can Help"

Still another experience: Something happened that led to Vellie being taken over by the remembered impact of her father's psychosis. She calmed down after a few hours, but each of us was affected. Over the next few days, we talked about it.

Late in the afternoon of the third day, I began pleading with Vellie to let me help her.

"This may be our last chance," I said.

I began to cry, saying, "I held your psychosis, the psychotic world you were in with your father. You haven't been able to let me help you free yourself from your entanglement with him."

My crying quieted down, and I heard my desperation. Helping Vellie by "holding her father's psychosis" was an effort to redo my drama with my mother. I could not fix her, but I was sure I could "fix" Vellie. I felt an unexpected sense of freedom. My life did not depend on "saving" Vellie.

My desperation was driven by another urgent need. I needed Vellie to recognize and validate a core of inner goodness in me. I needed her to do that to neutralize what I experienced as a core of badness permeated by shame.

But now, as I became aware of my urgency, I had a remarkable experience. I, myself, recognized within myself that very sense of goodness for which I had sought validation from Vellie. A rebirth of a core of myself emerged spontaneously, right there and then, in the context of our mutual respect, caring, and love.

A Primal Howl

Unexpectedly one evening, emotions relating to my "sticky things" memory burst out of me. A day or two before, I was at a town farm store near us, where I had the opportunity to observe a little boy, maybe six or seven years old, who was with his mother. Two or three other women working in the store knew him too. I was struck by the women's enjoyment of him and their affection, as well as his comfort in this little group. A distinct envy pulled at me.

On the day of the experience I am recounting, I was out of sorts in the morning, upset, and feeling like my day was ruined. After lunch, I rested, slept, and got up late in the afternoon.

On my way to my study, Vellie invited me to speak with her. She was concerned about what was going on with me.

"I don't feel good," I said in a feeble voice, not wanting to talk.

Vellie asked, "In what way, physically, emotionally? What?"

"I don't know," I said.

I went over to the windows, looked out at the meadows and woods, and to my surprise, I began to cry. I left the room and went to my study. I pulled my chair around so I could look out at the sky and our vista and feel the beauty. My crying deepened. I did not know what it was about. Vellie came in to be with me. She sat next to me, and occasionally she gently held my chest.

My crying turned into deep sobbing, and then I cried as never before. I bellowed, a screaming cry, and screamed, "NO." I went on for what seemed like a long time. An enormous output of sound and energy came out of me. I had not known my body was capable of such an output, and I was not forcing it.

The impression of the little boy in the store came to mind. The impression returned a few times, and I realized, "That's how it should have been."

I started shaking my head. I shook my head at the image of my mother disdainfully rejecting my dandelions. "No, it doesn't have to be like that. No, I am not bad. That way you look at me and reject me isn't right." Then I began screaming, "NO," over and over.

After a while, I heard a neighbor's dog howling a good quarter of a mile away. The slider was slightly open, and he heard me. Then I laughed and howled back a few times and gradually calmed down.

My primal crying came from all the times my heart shrank when I felt my mother's cross voice and her angry eyes. That was how "my day was ruined." Love and beauty had been together in my body, and that unity was shattered.

The Key

I have had the impression that – at some point – intense experience with my mother impinged on me more forcefully than might be suggested by the episodes I have described. A dream was the first key to the nature of that possibility.

> I am sitting at our kitchen table across from Vellie. Without warning, I suddenly feel a wave of a strange, awful feeling move through my diaphragm and chest. I am terribly frightened, in a strange panic. I must be about to die, then and there. I rise from my chair and reach towards Vellie. As I do, a piercing wave of the most awful feeling I have ever experienced goes through me. It appears as

if something horrible is happening to Vellie. She is transforming before my eyes. The feeling moves into my chest, a mix of horror and terror tinged with unreality. Vellie is sitting at the table without moving. She seems to be holding something with both hands, maybe an old brown pottery bowl. As I move towards her, I notice that her eyes are blank and unmoving. Now my terror is that she is dying … At this point I wake up.

I believe the effects of the uncanny and of horror reflect my reactions as a young child to my mother shifting into a disturbed emotional state in which she no longer sees me and is not in contact with me. Efforts at reestablishing contact by reaching to her would be met with a strange response or none, adding more fear. Suddenly Mother is a shapeshifter; she becomes a different, frightening, uncanny person whose look and appearance create dread and chaos.

From being her precious baby, my mother's perception of me changed – as I experienced it – to a brown, fecal thing, as if causing her shape shifting.

This kind of horror must have been the emotional trauma that left me frozen in my development as a separate self in relation to my mother. It created the conflict between my desperate need for contact with her and fear-driven avoidance to ensure I never again experienced such shocking disruptions and loss.

With Vellie, and others, I repeatedly experienced horror and a conflicting mix of desperate need and avoidance. When we were in Israel on Hapardess, I lived through those horrors and experienced a developmental separation. Vellie's presence made it possible then.

Torture

"You looked tortured when we first sat down." My best friend was telling me how I looked when I met him for lunch on one of our trips to the States. I knew I felt like hell.

Again, a disturbing dream – more of a nightmare – helped me acknowledge this experience.

> An agonizing experience. A woman – Vellie/Mother – is holding her hand on my left side, on my ribs just below my heart. This is creating a sensation that penetrates me, pushing a sensation of tickling into an agonizing, unnamable pain. I am writhing and trying to get away from her hand. Finally, I can say, "Take your hand away." She removes her hand, but I am still writhing and moaning. After she removes her hand, I begin to cry. The thought enters my mind (in my dream), "This is what happened to me."

The potential for feeling tortured lived in my inner world, a state regularly triggered in my relationships with women.

Trauma

One month in the past few years, two exercise injuries left me feeling shaky, fragile, and vulnerable. I felt weak, a bit frightened, and not quite fit to be in the world. I felt a slight quivering throughout my body. After a few days, I recognized it as the feeling of traumatic shock. I remember frequently feeling this way as a child in any but the most familiar and safe environments.

Adaptation

At some point in my childhood my vital connection with my mother was lost in a traumatic way. She was not able to help me negotiate a rapprochement, so I remained in aloneness. The break with her also left me in limbo with the sexual and erotic development that was underway in my relationship with her. With major developmental steps aborted or stalled, I lived in a state of vulnerability, shakiness, and uncertainty through childhood and into my adult life.

Instinctively, I did what boys do; I turned to my father. I connected myself with him to the degree he was available. My brother's impingement on me arrived as I was attempting to survive the Scylla and Charybdis of my parents. It left a scramble of distractions and further confusions. Out of my experience with him, my chthonic sexual persona took form.

Fortunately, my wishes for freedom, love, and happiness remained alive. Now, in this peaceful and fulfilled moment in my life, I have been able to put to rest this complex of disturbances that began so early in my childhood at my mother's knee.

CHAPTER 36

Freedom and Identity

Father as Koan

I knew him as my familiar "Dad," but not as a person. He was the steady father who was a secure presence and steadfast in providing a safe, comfortable home. He provided the financial security that allowed me to pursue my education as I chose. I was grateful and cared for him. It never occurred to me to relate my difficulties in life to him, and it did not occur to me to criticize him. He was a man who was strong enough to establish himself in the top tier in a tough workplace.

I loved him, probably until the evening he hit me. After that, my affection for him closed off, and I withdrew. But later, as I passed through stages of my adult years, it was important to me to stay in touch with him and to see him now and then.

When I make a focused effort to understand more about who he was in my life, I draw a blank. My mind comes to a halt. He is a koan.

Nostalgia

One day I became aware of a vague but well-known feeling – a tinge of grief, barrenness, and loneliness. I thought, "Wait a minute what is this? This is the feeling of missing my father."

I miss a connection that may never have been there to begin with or was too tenuous and intermittent to hold or be held by. Still, I find myself wishing he were with me. Sometimes, this feeling of missing is filled with regret, remorse, and guilt, and it interferes with my enjoyment of myself and my life.

Still, all in all, I had more of a connection with my father than I did with my mother. I have memories of happy times with him. A few times he walked with me to my favorite place, a nearby creek. The way went through our yard, and he inevitably stopped to pull a few weeds, while I waited impatiently. We crossed into a field near our house, and then he would take out his Lucky Strike cigarettes. With the first puff, I would catch the familiar pungent aroma indelibly associated with him.

Nostalgia and magic imbue my memory of a winter night when we were out on the dark, quiet street. The snow was piled high, there were halos around the streetlights, and my breath freshened with the brisk, sparkling air.

Fondness for my dad warms these memories. In the few quiet moments when we were together, I felt his heart. But these intermittent moments remain separate. They do not weave into a story of a lifelong connection between father and son, and this has always been a source of inner self-doubt and uncertainty.

My Jacob Moment

On a tour in Jordan our bus stopped by the stream where, according to the Bible, Jacob wrestled with the unknown stranger who might have been an angel. Afterwards, his hip was out of joint, so to entertain Vellie, I put on a suitable limp.

I wrestle with the stranger within me. My father-stranger does not reveal himself clearly, just as in the biblical story. The long struggle to free myself as a man is wearing, but there is freedom in the struggle.

For a couple of weeks in the past year, I was limping for real with a painful hip. I enjoyed the fantasy of life imitating a biblical story. A few mornings after my injury appeared, I used my hands to release tensions in the tendons and muscles in my groin. It was not painful, but I began to cry, fitfully at first, but then fully. I cried for being injured – I mean I cried for being sexually injured, not for muscle-tendon strains.

As my crying continued, my sorrow came to focus on the memory of my father hitting me. I was nine or ten. I had been wading around in my creek that day, and I cut the side of my foot on a piece of shale, which was as sharp as a knife. In the evening, when my father was home, my mother insisted I put iodine on it. I did not want to; iodine on an open cut hurts. I refused.

My mother would not put up with my disobedience. Irritably, on the edge of hysteria, she ordered my father to do it. She used just the tone that would mobilize him instantaneously.

Without saying a word, he came into my room. He did not coax or reassure, and he was not friendly. He was brutal. He grabbed me and dragged me crying and protesting into the bathroom. As I struggled, he batted me with the back of his hand across my head. While I was stunned, he applied the iodine and let me go.

My father said nothing during this "treatment." After, he expressed no sympathy, and he made no effort at repair. I do not remember my reaction. I believe I was numb, and I have no memories of what followed. I know I quieted down and did not make any further fuss.

In my Jacob moment, as I cried, feelings emerged I had not remembered. My father betrayed me. With my mother's urging he had been willing to violate my self-respect and use his greater physical force. In addition, he violated my trust, an unspoken assumption that we had a warm bond based on kindness and appreciation.

Worst of all, my father's actions demonstrated the cold reality that my mother's and father's care about me as a person did not stand up to the slightest test. My mother wanted to put me in my place, and my father needed to keep her calm. My feelings were not a factor in their equation. I was out in the cold and alone. The broken connection with my father left a void, which I attempted to fill with my brother.

This episode shifted my life course; more specifically, it sealed the course I was then tending toward. I grew quieter in relation to my parents – and everyone – more alone, and more withdrawn. By the time I was fourteen or fifteen, I was as silent as he was. I lived and managed my own life from then on.

A Gestalt Shift

I was talking with Vellie about my father when she said, "I have a thought. Suppose your father was the sick one."

I heard the thunderous silence of one hand clapping. And I took another small step toward freedom.

But still, the first thing I said was, "No. Mother was the sick one. We all knew that. Dad was solid and steady and took care of us."

With my automatic response I threw a block against Vellie's supposition. But at the same time, I had a queasy sensation that was also exhilarating. The truth in Vellie's supposition sent waves of uncanny, dangerous, and disloyal feelings through me.

My view of my mother and father had remained unchanged since I was a boy. My mother was "the problem." I sided with Dad and felt sorry for him. I viewed my mother as emotionally unstable, and I believed Dad carried the burden of taking care of her.

In my view, Mother maintained control in the family and kept us all subdued with her chronic state of being unwell. In my unsympathetic eyes, she was always on the edge of emotional or gastric distress. One scratchy word sent her reeling into misery and somatic suffering. Mother's emotional disturbances frightened my father, and he was at a loss about what to do with her when she did become upset.

But now! Suppose my father was "the sick one." The shift was unbelievable – unnerving. My father? – *My father?*

In my eyes, my parents' priority was to maintain a home sanitarium for Mother's perpetual convalescence, providing her with a quiet environment for her self-care. Now, stimulated by blasphemy, revisions of this understanding burst forth in my mind. Initial questions became certainties. I perceived the converse gestalt. Our whole family could be seen as the necessary buttress supporting and protecting my father's fragile ego, a refuge from his work world. His secret weaknesses and shames could be deftly concealed behind the curtain of family arrangements for taking care of Mother.

Now, in my mind, my father stood exposed. He was not the paragon of strength and rectitude on a pedestal, always to be looked up to. This obvious truth threw a glaring light on my understanding of myself. Much of my shame about myself derived from my failure to measure up to my idealized version of him.

Maybe my father's caretaking of Mother was not as heroic as I thought. Mother acted as though she was entitled to pampering and being catered to, and my father responded anxiously to these dicta. His alarm was not just concern about Mother's well-being. He was easily thrown into his own disturbance. So, a new picture of my dad is developing. It is freeing. He is not bad, he is not "sick," but he is not the noble paragon.

He carried himself quietly with a kind of aloofness or distance, and in his silence, he conveyed an inner, unexpressed negativity – towards my mother, and for that matter towards me. He did not talk, he did not smile or laugh, he did not cry, and he did not play or take time to enjoy himself. He did not read or expand his knowledge of the world or delve into other interests. He seemed to live as if he had lost his curiosity along with his playfulness and humor. His manner may have hidden an inner disturbance and suffering that he could never allow anyone to know.

With the gestalt shift of my perceptions of my father and mother, the idealized image of my father broke apart. He was not an unwavering pillar of strength and source of validation. He needed his wife to take care of his world and give him a secure base to come home to. She kept Dad together.

A Father's Presence

My father disappeared in the haze of my idealization. Memories and perceptions of my experience with him disappeared, as if into the air, or into the wallpaper. I saw "Dad," but I did not see the man who was my father, leaving the enigma of an effect with an invisible cause.

The one thing that perhaps most affected me was just that – my father's invisibility. He was physically constant and present, but he was absent as a person. His not speaking was the largest element in his absence, but it was not the only one. Equally, and perhaps even more unnerving was his character-istic expression, which was neutral – a nonexpression. He did not look angry, he did not look sad, and he certainly did not look happy or pleased. His look did not express happiness or approval in what he saw, including me.

In relation to me, his characteristic expression became a question in my mind. "Is this boy going to measure up?" This boy was uncertain on that very point. I translated the signals I did and did not pick up into my self-doubt, which eventually edged into self-hate, and my excessive drivenness about work.

He did not identify with a culture, religiously or ethnically. He never breathed a word to do with Judaism. He did not read apart from the *Buffalo Evening News* and *Chemical Engineering News*, and there were no discussions about "life."

He did not reveal feelings, and he gave no indication that he had feelings, except for the times he grew angry or was upset about Mother. He did not overtly express love, affection, or sexuality.

Ravaged Interior

I felt secure living in my father's house, but living in the aura of my father's presence affected me badly. I became like him. I did not know how to express feelings. I did not know how to talk with others. I learned how to not talk. But there was a more damaging outcome: my interior self felt torn up, ravaged. This was the immediate impact of being around him, combined with internalizing his unexpressed and unacknowledged emotional being. A dream of a ravaged interior:

> I find myself in my childhood home, in my bedroom, the bedroom I shared with my brother. No one is there. It seems that the house had been rented out, and the tenant left the room in a mess. Everything looks old and worn. A small pile of trash is on the floor, not swept up, and a cigarette is stubbed out in it. There is a piece of old furniture and something most unusual: I look at the bed in the room, and I think, "It is still frozen." There is ice in the mattress and hanging under it, still melting.

I find myself in my familiar childhood home and bedroom, but the room is broken up, old, trashed and misused, and abandoned by uncaring renters. The uncanny phenomenon of the frozen bed, the room's emptiness, and its neglect and careless abandonment – together project a note of horror. This is my father's house, mine and my brother's room, my father's cigarette stuck in the trash. The room is me.

The scene is a unique telling of the story of my sexuality and my self. I hardly owned my own body, self, and sexuality before it was taken over by others, used, and I was left trashed and frozen – ravaged.

Frightening Impulses

My three family connections – mother, father, brother – were each disrupted and broken in their own difficult, confusing way. The shock with my father, described above, followed the shock of the disconnect with my mother. With my father, the connection was so ambiguous and tenuous, that it left a shock in that way too. The energetic impact of my brother's constant presence during the first ten years of my life had its own discordant effect, and that mingled with my experience with my father. Under this double dose of overbearing energy, I survived by the suppression and cautious monitoring of my energy and expression.

As I matured, I became frightened of my impulses – anger and sex. In my dreams they morphed into frightening creatures threatening to attack me:

> I see a few big bull-like animals. They have an
> uncanny quality. One of them is coming towards me.
> It is dark gray and has an ugly shape. It is protrud-
> ing its head out in front of itself and sticking out

its tongue, like a male chasing a female on heat. Its eyes are beady and fiery. I wave my arms to shoo it away. Oddly, the animal and some others metamorphose into outdoor statues. They are now attractive statues with gray and green patina.

I "wave away" my sexual and angry impulses, and they freeze into sculptures, no longer sexually aggressive alive animals. I had little emotional contact or communication with either my father or my mother. As a result, experience of all kinds – thoughts, feelings, and body experiences – remained inside and became an inner world. Inevitably, because it remained unspoken and unheard, I felt that what was in me was dubious in nature and most probably bad, so I did not trust my body. This limited my ability to understand my inner world, and my movement towards bringing myself into a relationship with the social world was tentative and uncertain.

Going Back

Frequently in dreams, I am trying to "get back." In such dreams I wander off for unknown reasons. But then the wish to "go back" comes up, and I also have the strange feeling that I left my belongings "back there." Now I wish to retrieve them, but I have no idea where the "there" is.

I'm trying to figure out how to get back to "the gathering." I'm on my bicycle, which was once my brother's. The location seems to be my hometown, near the park. It starts raining. Now I need dry clothes. I don't know where to go. I want to find some comfortable, relaxed clothes like I wore when I was my beatnik self. But I find myself wearing a button-down shirt ... I wonder if a taxi would take me "back" to the place of the gathering – wherever that was.

I made getting back to myself and finding myself my mission in life. On this mission, I have explored my inner world, including seeking clues to myself in dreams. In my dreams I often glimpse and even experience (as I have been describing) losses, lostness, old horrors, fears, and the terrible conflicted knots that have been obstacles to my quest.

My Quest for Identity

Given who my father was and my relationship with him, my struggle with the lack of identity was predetermined. I sought and longed for the connection with him that I felt I had lost. It always seemed just beyond my grasp. I could not see that the father I had was not capable of being the one I sought. But he was not. He was steady and strong in what he did, but he lacked the inner resources that provide the basis for connection and meaning.

I described my horror at seeing him collapse under my brother's hostile attack (see Chapter 8, "Sonny"). That scene could have revealed to me that I had been standing on shaky ground, not the solid ground I had imagined. But I was not able to see, and I could not afford to conceive of his lack of inner resources, his lack of selfhood, and the long personal history by which he was left lacking. And he was not inclined to look into himself. No wonder I was so careful not to criticize my father!

In my experience of myself, I failed. I failed to make the connection with my father. I never considered the possibility that, as my father, he might have wished to find ways to foster a connection with me. In myself, I turned what I viewed as my failure into self-criticism and self-hate. Meaning, belief, and identity could barely get a foothold on these grounds. This was how great obstacles were left blocking my path to freedom.

Through my twenties, the lack of a sense of identity was the toughest obstacle in finding my way in the world. It was the handicap I took from my years growing up. Not knowing what I wanted to do tormented me and left me feeling unfit. I experienced this profound lack in myself as the cause of feeling terrible. The converse was true. I felt terrible because of inner disturbances, and those disturbances made it impossible for my life to unfold in a healthier way and for me to own it.

Born of my parents, my journey was shaped by their deficiencies. To find myself, I had to work my way through the horrors, terrors, pain, rage, and suffering implicit in who they were in their life with me. None of us knew anything about such matters. It took me all my life to learn.

Neither their times nor their personal inclinations led them to pursue a quest that would involve looking into their sexuality and development as children, or into their feelings, inner thoughts, dreams, and ways of experiencing themselves, their spouse, and their world.

My sexual desire, my sense of myself as a sexual being, and my longing for love left me restless, unsatisfied, and seeking. I found the ground for my identity by staying with my quest for love and for sexual fulfillment and by grounding that quest in my body. That was my path to freedom.

CHAPTER 37

Going On

Self-Study in a New Key

One day as I listened to Vellie talking about her family, a new perspective on my own came to mind. It focused on a family scene I described earlier, which occurred just before I left home for my first year in college. My brother, his wife, and his in-laws had come to our home to criticize and harangue our father for not giving them enough money while my brother was in medical school. As my brother and the others were leaving, I was horrified to see my father on his knees with his head buried in Mother's lap.

This troubling scene and a hurt in my heart were still fresh when I arrived at college. The whole scenario felt like a shameful family secret. I was ashamed of my family and of myself. My alienation was reinforced, and my loyalty left me feeling I could not claim my right to my own happiness and the freedom of my own movement.

Now, looking back, this new perspective was seeing my family in its social context. In this view, any pride my parents might have had in the family they created must have been dashed. They were humiliated by a family who had neither established a middle-class standing nor seen to the education of their children to anywhere near the level of my siblings and myself. And now they were parents whose oldest son rejected and hated them. They were left with a daughter who had her own family, which they were not as involved with, and an unformed adolescent son. They were left with their own unspoken inner pictures of themselves and the background of their families' histories of mental disturbances and my mother's errant father. From my mother's comments, I gathered that my father became depressed, although I don't know for how long. They were not people who knew how to communicate and talk through such an experience. I myself never spoke about it to a soul.

This perspective on my family stimulated feelings and memories that were troubling enough to engage me in a period of self-study in a way I had not experienced for several years. The outcome was a clearer picture of who I was at that time in my life and how I developed from that point. I had relied for my survival on a driven, joyless approach to life that I had taken over from my father. I did not know happiness, pleasure, or a creative approach to work life.

These were stark realizations, but this was self-study in a new key. In prior years I was under duress, sometimes severely so. Now I was stirred, but I was not suffering; and I was not in an inner turmoil and struggle with myself.

The whole process was exciting and interesting, and in itself it was healing and integrative. I felt it resulted in enhancements of my capacity to be happy, to have pleasurable feelings, and to enjoy being with Vellie.

I learned an unusual lesson from this period: I could not have done things in my life any differently. It has been easy for me to feel remorse and loss about choices I have made, and it has been easy to imagine what I might have done (if I had had a little more wherewithal) to make for very different, more pleasurable outcomes. This kind of fantasizing was never more than a protection against the disappointment I felt when I acknowledged who I was and that I had done the best I could. That whole statement – I did the best I could – has taken on a new meaning. It's the final word. Using fantasy and daydream to turn a past real event into a different event that didn't happen is only that – leaving reality for fantasy. It does not reveal possibilities that are still waiting to be actualized.

Full Circle

On three or four occasions, a brief utterance from Vellie has changed my life. On one occasion, it was a "No." On another occasion it was, "Suppose your father was the sick one."

But the happiest of all was, "You may."

Recently, another happy utterance brought us full circle. We were sitting on the couch smooching. She said, "Let's go in the bedroom, take off our clothes, and lie down." A happy feeling went through me, and I became happier as we did as she suggested.

At the same moment, I had an unusual image, almost a sensation. It was as if something like a square structure or frame dropped out of me. I do not know why it was that shape. But I do know it was the empty outline of an old sexual injury that I felt so painfully when we were in our apartment on Hapardess.

Wonder, Awe, and Gratitude

Years ago, Vellie wrote, "We will look back on these days in wonder." We look back in wonder on all our days. To wonder, I add awe and gratitude. I am grateful for our journey together and to be with Vellie in harmony and love. We continue together on this path, nurturing, supporting, and loving each other, and our energy keeps its sparkle.

I am grateful that I had the time, energy, and emotional resources to live through and grow in the course of a long, difficult development, traversing such rocky and uncertain ground. While demons dominated my life for many years, I say with a full heart that my better angels have blessed me with this time in my life.

For as long as we go on, we will go on.

PART X

Vellie

How could anyone fail to notice that
your loving is a miracle?

– Libby Roderick, *How Could Anyone* (1988)

CHAPTER 38

Dream Interrupted, Wishes Fulfilled

Melting Numbness

One night during the weeks when I was writing my final chapters, I had restless, disquieting feelings that kept me awake for hours. These feelings had no content; that is, they had no imagery, narrative, or meaning. At the same time, they felt meaningful, and I wanted to understand what they were about. My work with them is an example of how this work of self-study and self-development is continuous and ongoing. At this point my work is not driven by desperation arising from my inner world, and it is not painful. While there is not a finality to the work, there is an ongoing process of integration that allows for the continuation of the positive changes that have been my goal.

To begin to explore the meaning of this experience, I talked with Phil. As I talked, I noticed a heavy feeling in my body. What struck me immediately was that the words I used in earlier chapters – "confusion" and "ambiguity" – felt "light" in comparison with the heaviness I now felt.

I focused on my breathing, paid attention to my heavy body state, and let go of trying to know content. The heavy feeling evolved from a diffuse state to a more defined focus in the area from my navel to the crest of my pelvic bone, which I call my core. It then evolved into a blackness and a terrible feeling that felt connected to the blackness. I could not describe the feeling other than to say it was terrible.

Then there was a final shift from the blackness with its terrible feeling. The blackness dissolved, and I experienced a tense holding encasing my core. The holding had an energetic quality with feelings that ran from below my diaphragm to below my navel. Physically, the holding interfered with my breathing. I stayed with and identified these shifts in bodily sensations for over an hour.

As I continued to pay attention to my body state, I realized I was experiencing my numbness, and that my numbness is the tense holding around my core. Now I could see that my blankness and my muted sexual feeling resulted from my numbness. This is how I began to grasp the content.

Then it became clear to me that this holding around my core area (the numbing) was a self-protective response to threats experienced as a child to my existence as a person, as a self. And they occurred in my daily life in the family. The threats took various forms, but I was not exposed to physical violence.

With my eyes opened to this mundane reality of my daily life, it now seemed I had always known this. A long history of violations of my sexual development runs through my daily life in my family and in the culture that I was brought up in. It began at my birth with the disappointment about my gender. It continued through my developmental years and through my adolescence and the years when I was my father's caretaker. I lived that history within my family, and the threat was reinforced by the extended families. Whatever I encountered in my two high school years was the continuation of that daily life, but for those years significant memories are lacking.

A Girl's Dream and Its Interruption

From the time I was a little girl, my dream was to become a woman, have a loving man in my life, marry and have children – no doubt the dream of many little girls in all times and places. As an adolescent, I prayed, and I was serious in prayer, that I would have a man who loved me, was intelligent, and with whom I could live a secure, safe life.

That dream had been interrupted. At the time the interruptions occurred, I accepted the violations to myself and my sexual development as "normal daily life" within my family and my culture. Even when I was the object of my father's rage, my mother did not make a big thing about it, and she did not intervene or help me.

My father was always present in the family, so I did have the experience of having a father in my life. I have written of the few times when he was fatherly. It has been sad to realize he had little capacity to see another as a person separate from himself. He did not understand my need to have a caring, protective, and reliable father.

His disruptive behavior over the years showed no reasonable understanding of who I was as a child and adolescent. He often laughed at me, teased me, and humiliated me from my earliest years; he betrayed my love; he created threats; he made fun of my girlfriends; he became insulting if he heard me on the telephone with a friend; he undermined me as a girl by his intrusive involvement with the way I dressed; he demeaned every boy who came near me; and, on crucial occasions, he crushed me with his crazy rage when he learned I received a boy's attention.

When I was his caretaker, he did not show appreciation that might have led to my feeling that I could be a good wife and homemaker. On the contrary, I was left with a horrible emptiness about ever being able to cook or care for a home. Cooking became a frightening and often a tense, tortuous experience. The fear was not conscious so it took many life experiences to realize I would go blank when faced with having to cook for anyone other than Phil.

As I described previously, this was a difficult time in my father's life. He must have had the need to discharge his tension, irritability, and rage, and I was the only person there. His strange, probably psychotic, rage had so strong an impact on me that I was shocked and became dissociated. My brain functioning was disturbed, so I was unsure of my intelligence and my social ability.

I have said that I have no memories of physical sexual violation. But neither do I have memories of warm, supportive times, or moments of communication with a father who was interested in his daughter. He did not have a concept for that type of relationship - father, daughter. I do not remember having a meaningful conversation with him.

A Mother's Part

My mother had a way of distancing that had a subtle quality of making me feel she had difficulties in acknowledging my existence. This may have been partly a guilty response to my father and his family being angry with her for having another female child. And partly it may have been a characteristic resulting from her own traumatic childhood. Some of my own ways of distancing myself in relation to myself and others may have started by internalizing her distancing.

Mother would see her traumatized self in me, and that led to confusing ways of relating to me that undermined my sexual development. I needed her support to develop capacities for excitement, pleasure, happiness, and the wonders of being a young woman. I needed her to let me know that I was a lovely girl or young woman and to show that I gave her feelings of pleasure just for my being. I needed her smiles of enjoyment just for me. Sadly, she could not fulfill these essential needs that would have made a healthy development possible.

From Horrible to Hurt to Free

Another period of restlessness followed the one I just described. One morning I found myself feeling disturbed, and I knew that meant more changes. I was edgy, frustrated, defensive, and angry. I told Phil, "Well, the whole thing is about what a horrible person I am." Of course, I never wanted to reveal what a horrible person I am. I spent my whole life, first trying to be a good Christian girl, then just plain and simple a good person, and now a healthy feelingful person capable of self-love and love of Phil, one who continues her journey of self-development.

I barraged Phil with depictions of myself as a horrible person – beyond horrible. I told Phil it was obvious how I came to feel that way. I was made to feel I had done horrible things, and horrible became my identity. I reminded Phil of the many examples I have written about in my report.

Phil reminded me that in these significant examples one or another of my parents had directed hateful anger at me, which frightened me and went deep into my being – heart, genitals, and soul. Even now, I become tense and numb remembering the times my father had crushed my excitement as a girl and as an adolescent.

As we talked, I became more and more upset and tearful. I felt an awful hurt. Now I did not feel horrible; I cried and felt hurt. I felt the cruelty of what had been done to me, and how inconceivable it is that a parent would treat a child in that manner. My whole history of cruel violations of me and my sexual development became real to me. *I hurt.* I could call these horrible experiences "ordinary life" only because my feelings had been so muted. Now I could cry for myself, and I could emerge from my identity as the horrible person.

A Soul Survives

Growing up in my parents' house, living with their unresolved traumas, left me seriously handicapped for life in the world as an adult. My self-agency – the feeling of the right to be an autonomous person, free to exercise the aggression a woman needs to have and fulfill her own life – was cruelly injured. I claim that my sexual identity as a woman is the ground from which my self and my soul spring. The violations, interruptions, and attacks on my developing sexuality were assaults on my soul.

At the time I finished college, I hung in a precarious balance. I had always been aware of my mother's suffering, her struggles to manage financially, and her longing for help. I was also aware of my father's anxiety and neediness around his survival. He had primed me to stay home, add to the family income, and stay with them for the ongoing support they would need as they became older.

On the other side of the balance was my survival as a self for myself. My mother had provided a model for a daughter leaving home. With excitement she told stories about leaving home to go to college in another state. These stories made an impression on me. She was speaking of *freedom.* Her example and my own wishes to preserve my opportunities for survival and to be free were enough to tip the scales in favor of my leaving for Denver three months after graduating from college.

I left my family and their culture to escape the fate of staying in the family home, remaining single, and never realizing my dreams. I was able to mobilize my remaining strengths to begin awakening my wishes that had been blocked.

I started life with the feeling of being the wrong one. I am now free of that inner sense of who I am. No longer am I the wrong one, nor for that matter do I feel myself as the "right one;" I feel myself. My journey with Phil supported me while I found my way to a happier, freer, and more fulfilling life. Words cannot express my appreciation and gratitude that I was able to pursue my journey and that Phil and I have accompanied each other.

My goals were to be able to love and be loved. The moments when I felt my pleasure in being alive, in being female, and being a sexual woman were essential. Self-respect and self-compassion were guides to self-acceptance. As I developed self-agency and a sense of safety, I claimed my own space in my world. Over the years of our self-study, as the peace and ease I was able to find grew stronger and became my everyday life, my heart was opening to myself and to Phil. I experience my life with Phil as precious, and I have love in my heart that will remain with me as long as I live.

PART XI

Vellie and Phil

Introduction to Notes and Glossary

We had ongoing talks all the time we were writing. The following notes and glossary are brief summaries of some of them.

Our Approach to Writing Our Reports

Getting Started

We were happy together and enjoying each other at the time we began to write what would become our reports. Over the previous years we had experienced seriously stressful times and difficulties individually and together. Now we could appreciate that by persisting in our program of self-study and working together, we had largely released ourselves from reliving the traumatic aspects of our pasts and freed ourselves from being subject to the out-of-control reactivity of their traumatic effects.

The phases, events, and themes of our lives that we had relived and worked through again and again over the years stood out vividly in our minds; scenes and pictures carrying an intense energy. Phil was carried into writing about them, an experience that was exciting and rewarding in its own right. He also discovered immediately that the writing was a practice that deepened and integrated the work he wrote about. Vellie read every chapter and we discussed them together.

Through this initial period, Vellie felt no inclination to follow suit. But towards the end of 2015, she hesitantly began to talk about it. She grappled with anxiety about her lack of experience as a writer and her insecurity about her competence in such a field. After observing Phil's enthusiasm, she was carried forward by seeing that for her too writing might be an exciting and creative way to become known as a person – for herself and for Phil.

Phil read every draft of every one of Vellie's chapters, just as she did for Phil, and he saw that each of Vellie's chapters was a small jewel. They reflected Vellie's depth of emotion and of her soul, her honesty, her wish to be free from her early traumas, and the genuineness of her longing to love and be loved.

The initial title of the book was *Our Quest for Love and Discovery of Ourselves: The Intimate Journey of Two Psychotherapists.* By May 2015, we had drafts of a sufficient number of chapters to draw up a table of contents. Our grasp of what we wanted to express and our goal for our writing each chapter developed as we went on, and we wrote and rewrote every chapter three or four times to describe our experience with concise emotional focus. In 2018, Phil attended a workshop for writers in medicine and health care. He returned home and began all over again.

Resulting Characteristics of the Reports

Writing as Self-Study

We soon realized that writing and our sharing back and forth were perfect self-study practices for this period in our development and our lives. The issues we had addressed in previous years took on greater clarity and focus; they became more real to us as events we had lived through, and in the way we experienced their effects on us. In the course of this work, deeper levels of the emotions associated with our past opened. The figures of our past became more vivid. We understood and felt more. We each found that our sense of self deepened and strengthened.

The main purpose of our self-study work (to support the development of our capacity for love) guided our writing. This meant that our writing was for ourselves and each other. Although Phil had thoughts that the reports could bring attention to matters he cared about – the nature of the process of relationship change and of individual change within the relationship – our writing was not guided by considerations of publication and marketing.

Our reports have a few other features that are inevitable in the light of how we started and how we went about our writing.

Narrative

Our reports each have a protagonist, and perhaps the relationship itself is a third protagonist. The reports are about how all three protagonists grapple with a basic dilemma. Given the disturbances present and the dearth of resources in all three, can their wishes to love and be loved ever find fulfillment? This dilemma is present from beginning to end. It is existential; it is their reality. Change occurs in all three; we call the type of change that occurs "emergent evolution." The dilemma does not change

A Psychological Point of View

There are a number of possible actions available to two people facing this kind of dilemma, including the choice of no action. We never questioned that our choice of action would be to address our dilemma from a psychological point of view. That means the unquestioned focus for each of us is on our own selves and that we had the unquestioned faith that resolution lies through the process of deep change of our inner selves, body, mind, and soul. Our various self-study practices were our vehicles and methods for taking autonomous action and exercising our own self-efficacy in facing our dilemma.

Structure and Method

All these factors lead to how our chapters are structured and written and the relationship among chapters.

In every chapter and often in every chapter section, there is a focus on describing an experience. Usually, these descriptions begin with a body state. We do not begin with "why?" We begin with "what?" "What do I feel in my body?" We proceed from there by holding the experience; that is, staying with it, allowing any changes in the bodily state to emerge into awareness, and staying with the bodily states and any feelings that may accompany them, often bringing with them a memory of a past relationship. Because each chapter and chapter section begin with and focus on one particular body state or experience, each chapter can stand on its own.

In a chapter or chapter section the descriptions of particular experiences become nodes in the flow of our earlier lives, often coming into and becoming nodes in our ongoing life. The connection between all these nodes is psychological. They all address our main theme – freeing ourselves from our pasts – and one or more of our several subthemes: parental and sibling relationships, sexuality, how we experience ourselves, and our perception of each other.

Difficult Reading

We have learned why some may find our reports difficult reading. Many people have experienced developmental traumas similar to ours and descriptions of these traumas can make difficult reading because they stir painful memories and feelings in the reader. (If that happens, it could be taken as an opportunity to work through that pain and those memories.)

We describe the pain, disturbance, and fear we went through. We wrote about these experiences as matter-of-factly as we could. It is not our intention to seek pity, appear to be martyrs, or even to make exaggerated claims as survivors. We tried to describe our reality. When we were able to incorporate our pain into a self-study process, it changed the way we experienced that pain. We knew that we were in a process of change and of freeing ourselves. Also, our pain dissipated over time; we are not afraid of it now or afraid it will come back. These experiences had been internalized as children. This is our history. Our work enabled us to integrate those experiences freed from their traumatic effects.This is how the process of growth works. A certain joy and fulfillment are a part of that process.

Finally, a reader might get the feeling that we go "round and round." This is true in a way, and it reflects an aspect of any self-study process. For example, Phil might work with and resolve some particular difficulty he has with Vellie. He feels wonderful about having resolved it, perhaps by resolving some aspect of his relationship with his mother. Does that mean he will never again find himself in the same difficulty? Not at all. Until the deeper emotional layers of the issue have been opened, it will come around again. Each time will be different. The circles are not just circles going "round and round," they are part of a spiral that keeps opening outward and expanding like the chambered nautilus "building more stately mansions."[6]

---

[6] From "The Chambered Nautilus" (1858), by Oliver Wendell Holmes. Retrieved from www.poetryfoundation.org/poems/44379/the-chambered-nautilus.

NOTES 2

Psychedelic Experience

Psychedelic experiences are often surprising and unexpected revelations. We felt fortunate and excited to have these substances available. We incorporated the use of LSD, MDMA, and marijuana into our self-study work because we found they were powerful tools in helping to resolve the effects of our childhood and adolescent traumas.

They are unique kinds of experience, and we treated them as such in the way we worked with them. We usually entered an experience generated by one of these substances with some idea in mind of what we wanted to learn about ourselves, our pasts, and our relationship with each other. Once we felt the effects of the drug, we gave in to it, letting it guide us. We never had a bad trip or felt threatened. As the experience went on, we would usually make contact with each other and share what we were experiencing. This kept us grounded, helped the experience to become a part of ourselves, and deepened our connection.

The energetic vitality of the psychedelic experience energized and freshened our interest and motivation in our daily self-study work. These exciting experiences stimulated us for a period of days and weeks afterwards, and often we returned to their imagery and the memory of the intense effects months and even years later.

When we say they are a unique kind of experience, we are comparing them with other kinds of experiences we explore in their own unique ways. For example, one common type of experience we work with is the difficult feelings of all kinds that come up in the ordinary course of our lives. With these daily life experiences, we usually begin with talking with each other, which sharpens and focusses the issue. From there we may move to self-directed work with the body and with the associated emotions that emerge. This can lead to establishing the place of the experience in our memory of our earlier life, and this establishes a broader life context in terms of which we can understand the experience. Usually, we are aware of an emotional, energetic process that often continues for several days. We work with a psychedelic experience following the same model we use in working with our daily life experience.

Dreams and memories (bodily or pictorial) are two other kinds of distinct experiences we work with, proceeding in a similar manner. Finally, we consider that psychedelic experiences are unique in their own way, and we work with them in such a way as to respect the experience as it is and for what it is. We do not stretch them into other meanings in a way that is different from working with other kinds of experiences. And we certainly do not dismiss them because they occurred while using the psychedelic substance.

At every step of the way, we ground our working process in our awareness of our body. This is the best guarantee that we will stay focused on a meaningful path that will lead in the direction of our goals.

Each of the three substances – LSD, MDMA, and marijuana – tend to give rise to different types of experience: Marijuana tends to heighten awareness and feelings in the body, usually eliciting sexual feelings and feelings and memories connected with sexual development.

MDMA also heightens bodily sensation and awareness. It tends to open the heart to one's self[7] and to the other, stimulates an exciting, pleasurable flow of energy, and opening to deeply positive feelings within the self.

LSD generally seems to bring at least two different types of experiences. In one, the perception is of the outer world, and awesome beauty and wonder may be revealed to our senses; or the experience may arise from the inner world and the past that are projected as being in the here and now.

We came to understand our LSD experiences as examples of a unique form of remembering that was typical for us with our histories of traumas. Typically, we experienced enactments that emerged spontaneously as expressions of a past traumatic event. They were accompanied by heightened affects, movement (of the enactments), other sensory feelings, and even momentary

---

[7] See Glossary, "oneself vs. one's self."

physical changes – all of which we can understand as being derived from the original experience of the event.

Regarding physical changes, one is recorded in Vellie's section, "Phil, I Have a Secret." Phil desribes how Vellie's appearance changed. Vellie remembers two times when she saw Phil's physical appearance change. In one, she saw him as how he would be if his body had filled out developmentally, with good nutrition. He looked full and muscular, not so thin and delicate. On another occasion when Phil was on the floor remembering his grandfather, Vellie saw him as a thin, old man, an image of his grandtather that he might have internalized.

With two caveats, we keep in mind questions about the veridicality of a psychedelic experience. The reality to which we compare a psychedelic experience is our own personal reality. We do not have some "objective" reality apart from that. We have the same view of the veridicality of our conscious memories – both recent and from long ago. For that matter, we view descriptions of here and now experience in light of the same questions and caveats.

The importance of exploring any form of experience for us has to do with furthering contact with and understanding of ourselves. Psychedelic experiences have shed "light on hidden darkness" relating to past trauma. We assess the meaning and veridicality of our understanding and view of any experience based on its relationship to our overall understanding of ourselves and our reality as already known. We believe that bringing the work and awareness back to our bodily experience is the final guarantee confirming the meaning and veridicality of our understanding, and it establishes the basis for our knowing that we are on the right path for our change process to be in line with our positive development.

NOTES 3

Implications

The Laboratory of the Couple

For both individuals, joining together as a couple results in all kinds of hitherto unfamiliar experiences. In favorable circumstances, many of them are delightful, and this was certainly the case for us. For some couples the experiences produced are not only unfamiliar but frequently unpleasant, sometimes extremely so, and this too was the case for us. Here, a common reaction is: "I don't want or need this. This is not what I signed up for." However, like any new and unexplored experience, they offer the opportunity for exploration and learning something new – in this case, about oneself.

Phil has likened the couple to a laboratory that spontaneously produces its own experiments. This does not happen by choice. It is inevitable. It is a function of our development and our resulting personalities or characters. These highly energetic emotional structures engage with each other and bring out emotions, traumas, loves, and hates that are left in them from childhood, adolescence, and early youth. Our reports illustrate this.

On the Process of Change

Along the way we often noted how much time we spent managing conflict and painful emotions. This involved a great deal of talking together and time on our own.

We wondered if other people spent as much time on their relationship as we did. We believed the time and energy we invested in ourselves was the best of all possible investments.

We were disconcerted and often alarmed by our unhappiness, our inner pain that we experienced bodily, the intensity of our rage, and our self-hate. Again, we wondered if others experienced as much distress. In any case, it was evident that for us the work requisite for happiness and love involved facing and experiencing a great deal of pain. We wondered if there were other therapists who had worked through similar experience.

Often, we felt that we were suffering for love, and this went against the grain. To be loved seems like a biological "right," even if the capacity to love and be loved has not developed naturally from early on. Because of that, however, our commitment to our goals demanded a difficult and painful journey guided by a belief in goodness and the possibility of love.[8]

On Autonomy

After many years in therapy and training, we still had serious problems, and we were on our own. If we were ever going to overcome them, we had to rely on ourselves and each other. In the end, this proved to be the best condition for positive change.

Once we were on our own, we began learning that the development of autonomy and the capacity for self-agency were our most important developments. This meant that we had to change, and the only ones who were going to initiate and follow through on changing were ourselves. Each of us had to do our work, and a major part of that work was learning how to take responsibility for our own inner experience as well as our behavior.

Autonomous functioning means assuming responsibility for our every act and feeling. This does not mean being in control of them. We rarely were. It does mean that we cannot blame the other (or our history). It means taking ownership, and it meant that developmental work and self-study are ongoing.

We learned to claim the experience and development of self-agency. We experience this as the felt sense of competence to manage in the world. We experienced how the development of the sense of self-agency depends on the development of autonomy, and self-agency supports the capacity to act

8 Many, if not most, people probably enter adulthood capable of developing within a couple with much more pleasure and far less difficulty than we experienced. We believe that they probably had the good fortune of family and parental relationships that facilitated that kind of healthy development.

autonomously. Developing the capacity for self-agency is continuous and ongoing. Effective self-agency depends on the capacity to mobilize necessary aggression to overcome obstacles to making one's place in the world and to meeting one's needs. Autonomy and self-agency are functional aspects of the self.

Our self-study practices took the place of our therapists. We believe that over time a competent use of our practices, or similar ones, can be learned and applied by a reasonably competent and attentive person. Self-study is the study of experience, not the application of professional knowledge. Our practices help experience of the self evolve and change. The important relationship is with the self. This allows the boundaries of the inner self to expand, making for a stronger, freer self.

Therapy As If Being a Person Matters

The implications of this slogan point to the centrality of the self. The word "self" refers to the individual human person. We understand the self as the initiator of actions of all kinds. I am the actor on my own behalf. This is the basis for autonomy: that I own and assume ownership of all my inner experiences and behaviors. I may act without thinking, impulsively, deliberately, fail to act, or be unconscious of the sources of my actions. All are still my actions.[9] The discussions of the therapeutic process and autonomy are all about aspects of the development and functioning of the self in his or her social environment.

When we wondered about spending so much time on our relationship, we were questioning the validity of spending so much time on ourselves, because that's what was happening. We each were very involved with the other and what went on between us, but we are two separate selves, two people, and any time spent was time spent on oneself; and the energy invested was energy invested in the self.

When either of us struggled with some experience in our daily relationship, the locus of that experience and its source of energy was the individual self and the individual body. There are two bodies, each a source of energy, a locus of emotion, and the originator of actions. This conception brings self-study, personal development, and relationship development into the everyday, the ordinary. It's just me and you, the two of us.

---

9 See Ana-Maria Rizzuto, W. W. Meissner, and Dan H. Buie, The Psychodynamics of Human Aggression (New York: Bruner-Routledge, 2004).

But remarkable things happen when it's the two of us. We experienced and report on many varieties of such happenings. The basic lesson of each event is the same: This is how the human being is. We thought the best idea is to learn to accept and enjoy – and love both self and other.

Sex and Aggression

Sex and aggression are fundamental biopsychological dimensions for understanding experience and behavior. We think of sex as referring to an individual's ways and choices of regulating and expressing sexual excitement, desire, and needs – the direct forms of energetic discharge. It also refers to the individual's full range of erotic capability. For most of our working careers, we understood liberating the individual's sexual manifestations from fear and unbearable conflicts of various kinds to be the ultimate goal of therapy. We noted the interdependence between the development of self-respect and sexual development.

As we went along, we learned about the development and deficits of our aggression and how it functioned. We were helped in this by the understanding that aggression is the biologically based capacity of the individual to confront obstacles to the completion of a desired action. It does not mean hostility or destructiveness.[10]

Obstacles can be inner or outer. From our psychological point of view in this report, we are most involved with inner obstacles. The extra push and energy needed to make a place in the social world or to meet an important aim draws on aggression. Aggression is often motivated by the effort to overcome damage to one's sense of self.

A person (self) who has the freedom to call on his or her aggression in a healthy and appropriate way will be a person (self) with strength, resilience, and the competence to manage in the social world. He or she will have the capability, for example, to manage a work life and to negotiate a fulfilling sexual relationship. Therapeutic and self-development work aims to foster that capability.

The Complications of Talking about the Self

The self is a necessary concept. It brings coherence and organization to any meaningful discussion of the person – myself or another. We identify the ineluctable inner state or feeling that we identify as "me," or "I," "myself," as well as "mine." We understand that state as the basis for those words.

---

10   See Rizzuto et al., The Psychodynamics of Human Aggression.

The perception of one's self or another is a wholistic gestalt. That means it is a construction of the mind that results from the unconscious integration of an array of information from multiple sources within the organism and feedback to the organism from the outer world. A wholistic gestalt cannot be put together piece by piece; it is a whole that is greater than the sum of its parts.

Complexity typifies the wholistic gestalt of the self. It is also characterized by a degree of ambiguity. Phenomena related to the self easily slip from one gestalt to another, so that, for example, behavior that might be seen as self-defeating can, from another perspective, be seen as containing the seed for positive growth. Each perception is valid.

The self changes in various ways over time. There are changes constantly occurring over very short periods of time and changes occurring over longer, and even very long, periods of time.

Two features of the self seem to pose unsolvable conundrums. The self is both bodily and psychological. It can be viewed from the point of view of subjective phenomenology or from an objective point of view, from the outside, so to speak, by another or by oneself. These apparent conundrums are the source of an intellectual history that goes back to the Greek philosophers and continues today.

A traditional solution has been to declare that the mind and body are the same, and at the same time, they are different. There is unity and there is a dialectical dynamism through which two different things are integrated. This is a very elegant solution, but it is virtually impossible to grasp what it means.

There is an entirely different solution that dissolves such conundrums. Different languages describe the various phenomena (body–mind, subjective–objective) characteristic of the self. These languages are not different languages the way English and French are two different languages. They are both English (or other); and they are different languages in the same way that the "language" of color is different from the "language" of form. The differences in the way we perceive these two different sets (body–mind, color–form) are expressed through the differences in the ways in which we speak about them and the implicit rules or criteria for ways of describing them.

Any shift in the language is expressing a shift in perspective and phenomenological point of view. For example, we can say, "This is a bright red." We wouldn't ordinarily say, "This is a square red," any more than we would ordinarily say, "This is a bright square." So, from one perspective we speak about the somatic aspects of the self, and when we speak about the psychological aspects of the self it reflects a shift in perspective.

There are other perspectives in the observation of the self. One of them has to do with the "psychodynamics" of the self. These are observations of the interaction of the forces that operate within the self. Another has to do with the functions of the self. This includes the function of the self from an evolutionary point of view. It also includes the functions of the self from the point of view of the individual's adaptation within their family and culture.

The category of phenomena with which bioenergetics deals are energetic phenomena. This category includes the ongoing daily process of dynamic forms and expressions of vitality (including restrictive tensions) and their development. It includes phenomena relating to the individual's sexual functioning and their capacity for sexual expression and their capacity for love. Observing these phenomena reflect the energetic point of view.

The self is never a unified coherent, consistent process. We should speak of the self-system. We can say there are subselves or aspects of the self that may be in conflict, and they may not be within the individual's awareness. Desired changes can occur with deliberative, focused self-study. The time, effort, and difficulty of the process can rarely be known beforehand. The deepest aspect of change is not a voluntary process. It proceeds in its own, sometimes surprising, ways. The most difficult, negative aspects of the self often hide the basis for positive growth and development; so, often, it is impossible to guess the path to desired change.

Vitality

Vitality refers to aliveness. That something – a person, animal, or plant – is alive is a perceptual given. It is not inferred. We know immediately that the most "life-like" mannequin is not alive. Aliveness is a fundamental aspect of the gestalt of the perception of self and other.[11] However, as with other aspects, aliveness is not experienced as a separate characteristic. Aliveness is embodied. That means that aliveness is "shaped" in the body. The forces shap-

---

11 See Daniel Stern, Forms of Vitality: Exploring Dynamic Experience in Psychology, the Arts, Psychotherapy, and Development (Oxford: Oxford University Press, 2010).

ing the body are biological, psychological, and developmental. The primary perceptual way in which we identify a given individual is the way aliveness is shaped in the body of that individual. The "shape" of aliveness is shown in the way – that is, how – the individual stands, moves, walks, talks, and even breathes.

What we have been calling "body affect" or "body memory" are subjective perceptions of forms of shaped aliveness. They are the "how" or "what" of individuals' experiences of themselves at a given moment. They are alive, embodied states, have characteristic levels of intensity (energy), and move or flow within the organism.

Love
On love, see Notes 4: Love.

Being With
After long experience we realized that being with the other person is the first and most important thing we could do with and for each other. Being with is a state of being in which both people in the couple have an awareness of themselves as being with the other and that the other is with them. The being with is here and now, ongoing. It is not an emotion and it is not an action, but it is a pleasurable, calm affective state. It may be experienced directly, and often it may be an ongoing underlying state giving a tone of well-being or comfort to life without being in immediate consciousness. Being with can also refer to being with oneself.

Parenting and therapy rest on the foundation of being with. With this condition the natural way of development is free to emerge.

NOTES 4

Love

Love as an Emergent Capacity

Most of these days there is a moment when I have stopped whatever I was doing and find myself gazing at Vellie. My heart and chest fill with the warm sweet feeling of love. I have no hesitation about naming what I experience as "love," just as I have no hesitation naming something red as red. Learning that what I experience is love may be more complex than learning that red is red, but they have something in common. In teaching a child the colors, we might point and say, "This is red," but the "this" referred to is not the color red, it is a red object, an example of something red. One cannot point to red as such.

Young children love, but when and how do they learn that that experience has a name, and its name is love? I remember one or two times in my life when I loved and I did not have the name for that experience, like when I fell in love with Miss Brown, my tenth-grade teacher.

As an adolescent and through my young adulthood, I was filled with longings – longings for a woman I could be intimate with. Even then, I was not inclined to say that I longed for love; I just longed. And that longing could be stirred up any time, and in fact colored my daily life. I did not make any interpretations of my longings, they felt like a given – this was my life: to long.

At some point I came to think of myself as trying to find love and that my longings were for love. I still did not have an understanding of my longings or how to make looking for love a practical goal. When Vellie and I first became a couple, in my own view of myself I did not know how to love. So my idea at that point was that I needed to learn to love. Fairly soon, I realized that love is not something you find, nor is it something you learn.

My task was a more humble one. I had to develop the capacity to love. Under good-enough circumstances, this capacity will begin to develop in early life. As with any capacity, from riding a bicycle to playing a musical instrument, it develops by practicing it – that is, living it. In early life, parental love of the young child provides the circumstances and the stimulus to initiate development of that capacity. Development of the capacity for love or developments interfering with that capacity will continue through the decades of development.

The capacity for love is an emergent capacity of the self. It develops and evolves as the person develops and evolves within their family and culture. I believe that most children, under good-enough circumstances will begin to develop the capacity for love. I also believe that it is a capacity that needs loving parenting and fortuitous circumstances to develop into adulthood. And I believe that when a child's inherent capacity to love is not met with an environment that facilitates that capacity in a good-enough way, the child may be left with the most unfortunate of all detrimental deficits.

These thoughts suggest another significant aspect of love, and I believe there is an abundance of illustrations of it in our reports. Healthy development in the two decades of human development depends on love. These years of development for most children will be filled with risk and jeopardy in any case, but development will stay on track for the most part, if the child has relationships – or even one relationship – where he or she is loved by a parent or other consistent caretaker. As I wrote earlier, children need love to grow in the same way that plants need light, air, and water. Without love, or with disrupted, intermittent love, the child will mature biologically into an adult – other conditions being satisfactory – but, like a tree deprived of water or light, that growth will be distorted or stunted to a greater or lesser degree.

Love and Evolution

The capacity for love can be considered an emergent process in terms of biological evolution. Most biologists seem to agree that it is a capacity found in other animals in some form. Love is a human capacity that evolved as our species evolved over hundreds of thousands and maybe millions of years. I believe we can say that it emerged, or began to emerge, as we became a species that invested decades in raising and parenting our young.

Saying love is an emergent process in biological evolution means that its evolution is distant from genetic selection and variation. It occurred as the biological evolution of our species began to occur in the context of our evolution of language and culture, each influencing the other.

Our reports are about what we had to do to resolve the obstacles that our childhood traumas left in the way of the development of the capacity for love. We had to find practices and a way of life that would allow as great a degree of support for that development in adulthood as possible.

It is difficult, if not impossible for the capacity for love to develop when the individual's life is dominated by issues of emotional survival, as typified by a life largely under the influence of traumatic childhood experience. In this instance, the individual's life reality has to do mainly with survival. In contrast, an inner sense of safety allows for the unimpeded development of the capacity for love. This means that the individual is living and functioning in some measure in an arena that is not dominated by the struggles for survival. Biologists speak of play as the type of behavior that occurs in a life arena that is safe. The safe "play space" allows for the development of the emergent trait of love.

Other Properties

Practice

Love is a practice. It is not learned, developed, or practiced under the stress of survival issues. Its practice lives in a relaxed zone, where survival issues are not foremost. The meaning of love, even the use of the word, is developed over time with experience in family and culture.

It is not an emotion, although it is certainly emotional, involving feeling, bodily arousal, and meaning. It is not a motivation, although it gives rise to motivations.

As a practice it is an encompassing integration of all levels of the self and organism – the whole psychoneurobiological system. As noted earlier, its function depends on a healthy development. It is impeded by any and all posttraumatic disturbance.

Sex

Our sexuality is deeply intertwined with the capacity to love – sometimes separate, sometimes indistinguishable. Disturbances of sexuality will impinge

on the capacity to love. For most human beings, when our sexual excitement
and love come together in relation with one chosen other it is a great happiness. This is a theme that runs through all cultures from time immemorial.

Empathy

Love is the deepest kind of empathy. The empathy of love is characterized
by a unique way of regarding the other, a cognitive attitude; we might call it
"cherishing" or "treasuring." The intensity of this empathy tends to expand
each other's boundaries so that, while each retains the experience of their
separateness, each can also have the experience that the other is part of
them and vice versa.

Self-Love

Self-love is a function of the self that is essential for the maintenance of the
self in a state of health and life satisfaction. Like other functions of the self
such as self-respect, it has a line of development that begins early in life and
continues evolving and maturing to the end of life. Its most active period
of maturation and importance for self-maintenance is in later mid-life and
continuing on from there. Just as with love for another, self-love is a state
of energetic organization that can emerge as the self is liberated from the
effects of trauma. I learned the most basic, simple meaning of self-love from
Vellie: self-love is opening one's heart to oneself. This can happen, and it is
a wonderful experience.

The Sacred

I am grateful and happy now that I do love. Nothing is more important to
me in my life. This means Vellie's importance and meaning in my life are
equivalent to the meaning and importance of my own life to myself.

Given that love is as important to me as my own life, I am inclined to
say that love touches into a realm of life that I would call sacred. I am not
relating sacred in this sense to any other religious meaning or symbols. I
have no justifications or reasons for saying love touches the realm of the
sacred; it is my belief and my view of the nature of what is sacred in my life.
[First person writing by Phil.]

Glossary

aggression We do not use the word "aggression" to refer to hostile, angry, destructive actions. *Aggression* is the biological capacity to "overcome any obstacle interfering with the completion of an intended internal or external action." Aggression is a motivation or put to the service of motivations. Any capacities available to an individual can be put to the service of aggression, from physical strength to intelligence. It is not necessarily characterized by a destructive attitude. The emotions that may accompany an aggressive action are themselves not aggression. Anger, for example, which may or may not accompany aggressive motivations, is not itself aggression.

Healthy development of the capacity for aggression is requisite to function effectively in the social world. In development, when aggression is inhibited, undermined, or severely crushed there are severe behavioral and emotional consequences. These include difficulties and inhibitions in functioning in virtually every arena in life, depression, and living with other painful affects, such as feeling crushed or humiliated. Joy, excitement, and fulfillment may accompany the fulfillment of positive actions supported by aggression (*see* Rizzuto et al., *The Dynamics of Human Aggression*, 2004).

affect Any feeling, emotion, or feeling states of the body can be called "affect." For our purposes, we have given slightly different meanings to the words affect, sensation, emotion, and feeling. All these states have a valence – that is, they feel good or bad, pleasurable or unpleasurable, and so on. Also, they all have various levels of arousal or intensity.

We have used the terms "body affect," "affect state," and "affect" as equivalents, and we have used these terms to refer to experiences that are distinctively different from what we usually refer to as sensation, emotion, or feeling. The experiences referred to by all these words are accompanied by slightly different body states and ways of conveying meaning, in their ordinary usage.

The experiences we label as "body affects" usually do not have names. They have valence along the dimension of pleasure to unpleasure or good to bad. They are usually experienced as having bodily location, but the location is not defined in terms of anatomical structure. They are usually experienced as *within* the body. They often have a diffuse quality – that is, spreading throughout the chest, abdomen, thorax, and so on. They are experienced as *of the self*; I identify a body affect as *me*. Often, complex states of the self involve both cognitions and body affects; and, with attention, the body affect can be experienced separately from the cognitions. This is a basic technique for understanding the meaning of the body affect, and might reveal meaning very different from the cognitions. Shame is a good example of such a complex state of the self (*see* body memory).

bioenergetic analysis The form of therapeutic treatment we practiced and developed, oriented to the body's expression of its aliveness as well psychological analysis (*see* somatic-energetic point of view).

body memory A body affect state can become a body memory, and it usually will when it is brought into the self-study process either by bioenergetic work or by talking with one's partner. It becomes a body memory when one can discover its meaning or identify the affect with a significant figure from one's earlier life. Our reports have several examples of work with body memory.

A body memory is a memory in the form of a unique body affect state. It is not a narrative or pictorial memory. Once an affect is identified as a body memory it can usually be related to narrative or pictorial memory. Body memory involves body affects rather than a picture or narrative.

Self-study techniques usually activate body memories. Bioenergetics pays particular attention to them. They can be brought to the surface by energetic activation through breathing and movement, and then they can be further worked with in such a way as to bring emotions to the surface. Marijuana and psychedelics usually evoke body memory.

identification with the genital Children identify themselves with their genitals between the ages of (roughly) four and six. "This is me," is the form of the identification; although, at this age, it is not expressed in words. It is a continuation of the development of an inner sense of identity based on bodily experience. The Oedipal phase of development is expressed in terms of relationships of love and competition. However, the essence of this period for the development of the self, which is based on bodily experience, is the identification with the genital. We want to note that this description does not exclude transgender or other identifications, nor does it make them abnormal compared with cis gender. It points to the overall complexities of this process in children and their many unique variations in experience. In workshops, we use a specific exercise to explore identification with the genital. The group will stand in a circle paying attention to their feet on the floor and their breathing. We allow the pelvis to swing gently to and fro, following the breath, bringing awareness and feeling to the pelvis. Everyone is invited to focus their attention on their genitals and at the same time say or think, "This is me." As an exploration, alone or in a group, the exercise often evokes a rich variety of feelings and attitudes.

internalization Refers to a set of psychoneurological processes whereby experience occurring in relationship with an external source is taken into and made a part of the self. It is a primary mechanism in development of the self. The term is regularly used in the context of the psychoanalytic approach to child development to describe and account for the effects on a child's development of experience with a particular caregiver. The developmental effects of an internalization depend on age and the conditions under which it occurs.

Experiences in a loving, respectful relationship result in an internalization that sustains a child's inner sense of feeling loved and soothed. Those occurring in the context of traumatic circumstances result in structures within the self that function with a negative impact on the child's movement and development, and they leave an inner experience of self-negativity in a variety of ways. The internalizations we write about in our reports show their complexity and pervasive negative impacts on our development. Internalization is the direct outcome of the somatic-energetic interaction between a parent and child, and indicates the way those interactions become established in very precise ways in the individual's psychoneurology – that is, in the brain, mind, and body.

love A unique energetic organization of the whole self and depends on the maturation and integration of the self. Its nature and power are apparent in how it functions in the life of the individual. The basic healthy development of the child depends on a facilitating environment where love outweighs trauma, stress, punishment, and being subject to parental trauma. Without that, the development of the capacity for love is distorted or stunted, both of which have far-reaching effects lasting the life of the individual. Life partnering in adulthood is the optimal milieu that fosters the development and enjoyment of the capacity for love. It is the ground for the personal growth of each partner. For the individual the capacity for love is the basis for a fulfilled life (*see* Note 4: Love).

Lowen, Alexander (b. 1910–d. 2008) Student of Wilhelm Reich. He developed bioenergetic analysis – a way of understanding the person based on the energetic processes of the body – and he introduced a therapeutic approach based on that understanding. He established the Institute for Bioenergetic Analysis in 1956, which became the International Institute for Bioenergetic Analysis in 1976. He wrote several books.

m&m Masturbation and marijuana; in other words, masturbation enhanced by marijuana.

myself vs. my self "My self" refers to a person's psychological self or spiritual being. "Myself" is a reflexive pronoun meaning the verb of the sentence refers to both subject and object.

oneself vs. one's self *See* myself vs. my self.

place names:

> **Hapardess** Our apartment on the street of that name, where we lived in Israel for the last six years of our time there. Hapardess means "the orchard" in Hebrew.
> **Happy Meadows** Our residence in North Carolina.
>
> **Kfar Saba** A large town north of Tel Aviv, where Hapardess is situated.
>
> **Pepperell** The small town in Massachusetts where we lived and owned a house for many years, about forty miles north and west of Boston/Cambridge.

Watertown The Massachusetts city across the Charles River from Boston, where Vellie had her little condo.

Reich, Wilhelm (b. 1897–d. 1957) Student of Freud. Through his clinical observations, he introduced into psychoanalysis an observational approach to understanding the somatic-energetic (bodily) processes occurring in analytic therapy. He developed the concept of character in psychoanalysis and demonstrated its somatic-energetic basis, and he introduced a systematic technique for therapeutic intervention. He described the centrality of sexuality in human functioning. His work is the foundation for bioenergetic analysis. He lived in American after the start of World War II (*see* somatic-energetic point of view).

self We use the word "self" in the ordinary way as referring to the individual person. The self is the person. As we write our report, it is filled with references to the self. We need to have the language of the self in order to write about what we write about. This indicates the centrality of the conception of self to our way of understanding of ourselves. We write about the development of ourselves; and we write about the inner forces, emotions, and obstacles we encounter within ourselves. This is the natural language of the self, and it is the language used in naturalistic observation of the self. This is the language we use when we want to write about all the matters that we convey in our reports.

That we speak and write this way does not mean there is an entity to postulate that is the self, unless we think of that entity as the sum of all the different ways we write, speak, and think about ourselves. It does mean that we can identify a variety of phenomena that are described when we write about the self:

- The self is the body.
- The self is complex, and we need to think of it as a "self-system."
- The subselves of the system may be conscious or unconscious; there may be conflict between subselves.
- The self is the locus of autonomy and self-efficacy. When I act, it is myself who chooses to take action. I may have reasons and motivations, but I am the one who takes action in relation to them.

- The self is identified by the uniquely sensed center of my subjective phenomenology, all that we might include when we use the word "me."
- When aggression is called for, I, as a person, draw on it in whatever way is suitable to the situation.
- We can speak of having a strong sense of self; and we can speak of someone lacking a sense of self.
- In self-study, I take myself as a set of psychological and somatic phenomena to be observed. Certain aspects of my somatic self may be observed by another person, such as bodily tensions. However, inner aspects of myself are not apparent to another person, and those aspects will be known only if I am willing to communicate them. To understand the more "objective" bodily expressions of the self, requires my communicating their connection with my inner self.

(*See* myself vs. my self and oneself vs. one's self.)

self-relation terms:

self-acceptance A conscious, positive, noncritical attitude towards one's self, body, and personality, in all its expressions. In self-acceptance, one acknowledges one's own experiences and behaviors in a matter-of-fact, friendly way as expressions of one's self, owning them in a positive way. Being self-accepting does not rule out self-assessment based on having standards of behavior.

self-compassion An accepting attitude of loving kindness towards one's self, including one's suffering and failures; acknowledgment that one's self is the same as all other selves in wishing for and deserving safety, happiness, health, and ease of living; and maintaining this attitude in regards to all of one's experiences and actions, whatever the outcomes.

self-esteem Self-esteem is a felt psychological attitude of self-evaluation, attributing value and worth to the self, either positive or negative, and in greater or lesser degrees. Self-esteem tends to be unstable and dependent on continuous positive feedback from the environment; therefore, it is usually accompanied by anxiety.

self-love Self-love is the natural outcome of the maturation and development of the self: nonerotic; nonnarcissistic; beyond acceptance, an actual energetic, bodily state of love directed to one's body and self. Self-love is a necessity for the full development and survival of the self.

self-respect

The self is the body, so self-respect is literally respect for one's own body, bodily states, feelings, and all the ways we subjectively experience ourselves. Self-respect develops from birth onward and can be followed in its own distinctive developmental track.

A range and variety of negative disturbances in development give rise to shame, guilt, humiliation, a negative sense of self, and other painful affect states. These disturbances stem from violations of sexuality and impeding aggressive movement.

It is an ongoing, underlying, unconscious body process or attitude, reflected in how one experience oneself and one's interpersonal behavior.

It is a capacity: the capacity to be in contact with, feel, and live according to bodily states. The capacity for self-respect depends on a healthy identification with the genital at the appropriate stage of development. Experience that infringes upon and violates the development of sexuality disturbs the development of the capacity for self-respect.

It does not mean always having a good feeling. It is not "self-esteem." It includes the capacity to experience, acknowledge, and tolerate painful and difficult states without avoidance, suppression, and self-deception.

Shame, humiliation, and self-hate are negative mirror-images of self-respect. Their developmental tracks mirror that of self-respect.

Self-respect is the basis for self-compassion; each can foster and engender the other.

Much of the healing benefits of psychotherapy depend on the development of self-respect and the amelioration of negative mirror-image states; that is, all forms of self-hate, humiliation, and shame.

By and large, people with a healthy capacity for self-respect will be able to manage in life (*see* Helfaer, *Sex and Self-Respect*, [1998] 2006, and papers on self-respect at www.sexandselfrespect.com; *see also* self-relation terms).

somatic-energetic point of view The core of bioenergetic therapy. A point of view is a way of looking. From the somatic-energetic point of view we observe the somatic and energetic aspects of the self. Bioenergetic analysis is the clinical and therapeutic application of that point of view. When we say that the body is the self, or vice versa, we are referring to the somatic-energetic aspects of the body. A person has the capacity for motility (movement) and self-expression through feeling. These are energetic aspects of the self; they are nonverbal, and they are experienced as of the self, as "me." As a somatic entity, the self also breathes and exchanges energy with the environment in other ways. Studying these energetic aspects of the self reveals a wide range of variations and a family of phenomena that characterizes the overall functioning of the individual. We consider this point of view in the context of the therapeutic relationship. Wilhelm Reich observed his psychoanalytic patients as they lay on the bed. He described physical aspects of his patients that were somatic expressions of their character, or way of being the world. He described patterns of muscular tensions and ways of holding the body. These served to suppress aliveness, expressivity, and motility. The name "muscular armor" is given to these patterns of muscular tension. They develop as adaptive strategies to protect the individual from pain arising from inner and outer sources. Reich developed a systematic therapeutic approach to working with muscular armor to free energetic holding for the purpose of increasing the individual's capacities for energetic expression, including sex, aggression, and love. He noted suppressed breathing as always central in holding patterns. His approach always kept a focus on breathing. Freeing breathing from tensions fostered greater energy throughout the organism of the self. There are many examples of the functional application of this point of view in our reports. This point of view is more fully described in Helfaer, *Sex and Self-Respect* ([1998] 2006) and in the books of Alexander Lowen, including *Fear of Life* (1980).

violations of sexuality Many of the obstacles we write about in our reports are the result of violations of sexuality. Overt sexual abuse is a violation of sexuality. There are many ways that parents can interfere with a child's developing sexuality, resulting in a wide range of negative emotional and physical experiences for the child. Parental (and others) behaviors of this sort manifest disrespect for the person of the child. Violations of sexuality affect the quality of identification with the genital. They are plentifully illustrated in our reports (*see* Helfaer, *Sex and Self-Respect*, [1998] 2006).

References

Buber, Martin. (1966). *The Way of Man: According to the Teaching of Hasidism*. New York: Citadel Press.

De Quincey, Thomas. [1856] (1983). *The Confessions of An English Opium Eater*. New York: Chelsea House.

Eliot, T. S. (2001). *Four Quartets*. London: Faber & Faber.

Freud, Sigmund. (1966). Three Essays on the Theory of Sexuality. In *Standard Edition of the Complete Psychological Works*, vol. 7. London: Hogarth Press.

Frewen, Paul and Lanius, Ruth. (2015). *Healing the Traumatized Self: Consciousness, Neuroscience, Treatment*. New York: W. W. Norton.

Helfaer, Philip M. [1998] (2006). *Sex and Self-Respect: The Quest for Personal Fulfillment*. Westport, CT: Praeger; Alachua, FL: Bioenergetics Press.

Lear, Jonathan. (1960). *Love and Its Place in Nature: A Philosophical Interpretation of Freudian Psychoanalysis*. New York: Noonday Press.

Lepore, Jill. (2018). *These Truths: A History of the United States*. New York: W. W. Norton.

Lowen, Alexander. (1980). *Fear of Life*. New York: Collier Books.

Paglia, Camille. (1990). *Sexual Personae: Art and Decadence from Nefertiti to Emily Dickinson*. New York: Vintage Books/Random House.

Rizzuto, Ana-Maria, Meissner, W. W., and Buie, Dan H. (2004). *The Dynamics of Human Aggression*. New York: Brunner-Routledge.

Roderick, Libby. (1988). "How Could Anyone?" Turtle Island Music. Anchorage, AK.

Rosen, Michael. (2008). *The Quest for Authenticity: The Thought of Reb Simhah Bunim*. Jerusalem/New York: Urim Publications.

Stern, Daniel. (2010). *Forms of Vitality: Exploring Dynamic Experience in Psychology, the Arts, Psychotherapy, and Development*. Oxford: Oxford University Press.

Suzuki, Shunryu. (1970). *Zen Mind, Beginner's Mind*. Ed. Trudy Dixon. New York: Walker/Weatherhill.

Smith, Lillian. [1949] (1961). *Killers of the Dream: Revised and Enlarged Edition*. Garden City, NY: Anchor Books.

Spivack, Kathleen. (1981). *Swimmer in the Spreading Dawn*. Cambridge, MA/Newton: Apple-Wood Books.

Spivack, Kathleen. (2016). *Unspeakable Things*. New York: Alfred Knopf.

Zornberg, Avivah Gottlieb. (2009). *The Murmuring Deep: Reflections on the Biblical Unconscious*. New York: Schocken Books.

Meet the Authors

PHILIP M HELFAER, PHD was active for 40 years in the practice and teaching of bioenergetic analysis, a body oriented psychotherapy. He summarized the first twenty-five years of his work in, *Sex and Self-Respect, the Quest for Personal Fulfillment*. In *Riding Dragons*, co-written with his wife, he takes the path less travelled: exploring his inner life and deeper self – as grounded in the body and in relationship with the world – to gain his capacity for love and intimacy. Now, at home with Vellie, he lives in the pleasure of their love.

VELLIE HELFAER, BSN, MSN: To her accomplishments as a psychotherapist and teacher in bioenergetic analysis, Vellie brought a lifelong passion for continuous inner development and a special gift for grounding self-development in her body experience. In *Riding Dragons*, she shares her profound journey – experiences and practices – to realize her capacities for love and the strength of her own being that had been traumatically supressed in her early years. She lives quietly with Philip enjoying their love and their connection with the natural beauty surrounding their green home in North Carolina.

CPSIA information can be obtained
at www.ICGtesting.com
Printed in the USA
LVHW081918280122
709359LV00016B/469